Access to Advanced Level Biology

Howard Bowen

Joan McTiernan

Ian Simons

Maria Whittington

Series editors:
Ted Lister and Janet Renshaw,
Trinity School, Leamington Spa

SIMON & SCHUSTER
EDUCATION

Contents

Chapter 1	Energy in the living world	2
Chapter 2	Food chains	14
Chapter 3	Exchange	19
Chapter 4	Control and coordination	30
Chapter 5	Genetics and inheritance	37
Chapter 6	Microbes	51
Glossary		61

Acknowledgements

The authors would like to thank the following for their kind permission to reproduce photographs: Tony Duffy/Allsport (Fig 1.12); David Hall/Panos Pictures (Fig 1.11); Walter Murray/NHPA (Fig 5.22); Novo Nordisk Pharmaceuticals Ltd (Fig 4.3); Geoff Tompkinson/Aspect Picture Lib. (Fig 1.6); M W Tweedie/NHPA (Fig 5.17).

Thanks are also due to pupils at Trinity School who trialled early versions of this material.

They also thank Mike Bailey, Keith Hirst and Ray Watkin for their kind permission to reproduce, on pages 3, 4 and 6, the diagrams, questions and table of Activities 53 and 55 in *Active Biology: Pupil's Book*, published by Hodder & Stoughton.

First published in 1992 in Great Britain by
Simon and Schuster Education
Campus 400, Maylands Avenue
Hemel Hempstead, Herts HP2 7EZ

Reprinted in 1994

A catalogue record for this book is available from the British Library

ISBN 07501 02659

Typeset by Jim Weaver Design
Illustrated by Tek-Art
Printed in Great Britain by St Edmundsbury Press Ltd
Bury St Edmunds, Suffolk

Introduction

This book is designed to help you get ready for a post-16 course in biology: A-level, A/S-level, BTEC, Scottish Higher, etc. It doesn't matter which course you will be following because this book stresses the principles of biology, which are the same for any course.

You can use this book before you begin your advanced course or during the first part of the course. It will also be useful for reference during your course.* *Access to Advanced Level: Biology* has been designed so that you can work through it on your own, so the answers to all the questions are at the end of each chapter. However, cheating won't help your understanding!

How to use this book

Teaching yourself how to do something needs confidence, which often needs developing. We suggest that you work through each section slowly and don't move on to the next section until you have correctly answered the questions. If you are getting most of them right you are doing well. But what if you aren't? One of the skills you will have to develop for advanced study is independent learning. There are a variety of approaches to explaining concepts and ours may not always be the best for you. At advanced level (and beyond), using other resources, such as standard text books, and reading on your own initiative, is going to give you a valuable skill and that essential ingredient, **confidence** in your ability to learn by yourself.

Good luck and enjoy your biology!

The authors and editors

*There is a glossary of important terms at the back of the book for you to refer to.

Chapter 1 Energy in the living world

Starting points

Do you understand the following terms: **photosynthesis, respiration, metabolism**? Write one or two sentences (no more) to explain what you understand by each term. Then check them against the glossary at the back of the book.

Energy from the Sun

All living organisms need a constant source of energy. All of this energy ultimately comes from the Sun.

Green plants have **chlorophyll**, a pigment that can absorb sunlight energy and store it in a chemical form (food) made by the process of **photosynthesis**. Plants build up and store food in this way for themselves and the rest of the living world, so they are called **producers**. Organisms that do not have such a pigment cannot tap the Sun's energy and must obtain energy from the food that they eat.

Animals obtain their energy by eating food that has been made by plants. They are called **consumers**. Transfer of energy in the form of food from plants to a variety of animals forms the basis of **food chains**. In plants and animals, energy to carry on cell processes comes from food, whether the food is made within the organism by photosynthesis or taken in from the environment (eaten).

An oak tree is a producer organism, but many cells in its roots, its trunk and its branches – all those cells that do not contain chlorophyll – function like the cells in a consumer. Even its green cells are consumers in the dark. They depend upon food made by photosynthesis until they are in the sunlight again. The release of energy from food occurs in all cells at all times, as long as they are alive, by the process of **respiration**.

1 Divide the following into producers and consumers: dog, thistle, blackbird, kangaroo.

The theme of this chapter is the energy relationships of the living world that exist through the processes of photosynthesis and respiration. Chapter 2 looks at the spread of this energy through food chains.

Photosynthesis

All living cells need energy. Except for a few bacteria that obtain energy from chemical reactions, all living cells use energy that originally came from the Sun. Only the green parts of plants can trap this solar energy whilst they carry out photosynthesis.

The discovery of photosynthesis

Read the passage and then answer the following questions.

In 1772 Joseph Priestley placed a shoot of mint in a container of water and inverted a glass jar over it so that air could not enter. To his surprise the shoot remained alive for several months. In another experiment he noted that a burning candle was quickly extinguished when covered with a jar. Then Priestley placed a shoot of mint under the jar, and in a few days the candle, when lighted, burned again for a short time.

The 'restored' air was, as he said, "not at all inconvenient to a mouse which I put into it". Other investigators, however, were unsuccessful when they attempted to repeat Priestley's experiments.

The reason for this failure became clear in 1779, when Jan Ingen-Housz found that plants behave in the way Priestley described only when they are exposed to sunlight.

In 1782 Senebier discovered that plants absorb carbon dioxide when in sunlight. In 1804 de Saussure showed that the increase in plant weight after exposure to sunlight is greater than the weight of the carbon dioxide taken in.

By 1845, Mayer was able to recognise that the essential steps in photosynthesis are the absorption of light energy and the transformation of this light energy into chemical energy, which is then stored in chemical compounds manufactured by the plant. The process can be represented by the following equation:

$$\text{carbon dioxide} + \text{water} \xrightarrow[\text{chlorophyll}]{\text{sunlight}} \text{glucose} + \text{oxygen}$$

$$6\,CO_2 + 6\,H_2O \rightarrow C_6H_{12}O_6 + 6\,O_2$$

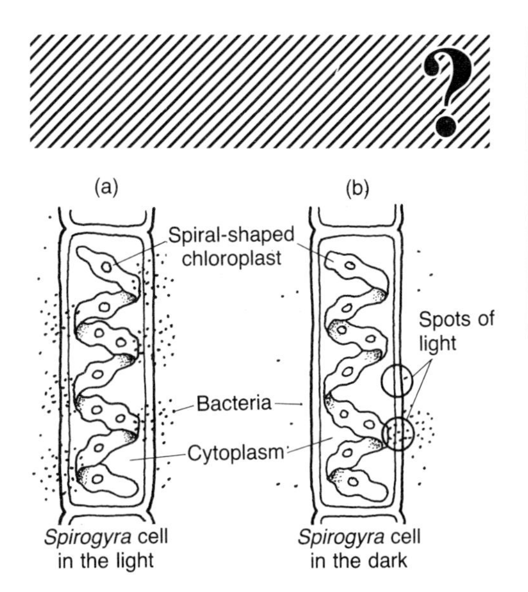

1.1 The alga *Spirogyra* and the position of swimming bacteria (a) in the light and (b) in the dark with two spots of light.

2 a What is the name of the gas that 'restored' the air in Priestley's experiment?

b Why did the mint plant only restore the air when it was in sunlight?

c What other substance is taken in by plants during photosynthesis to explain the further increase in plant weight observed by de Saussure?

Oxygen production in photosynthesis

In the 1880s a German biologist called Englemann carried out a number of ingenious experiments on photosynthesis. He used a freshwater alga called *Spirogyra* and a freshwater bacterium that can swim and move to regions of high oxygen concentration. Fig 1.1 shows what he saw when he (a) kept the *Spirogyra* and bacteria in bright light, and (b) shone two small spots of light on the *Spirogyra*.

3 a What do you notice about the distribution of the bacteria

(i) in the light

(ii) in the dark with two spots of light?

b Which part of the *Spirogyra* cell is responsible for producing oxygen? Explain how you worked this out.

c 'Oxygen is only produced in the light when a plant is photosynthesising.' Why do you think Englemann's experiment shows this?

d A prism can split light up into the different colours of the rainbow. Design an experiment using Englemann's basic idea to find out whether red, yellow, green or blue light is the best for photosynthesis.
(i) What measurements would you make?
(ii) Some tomato growers use electric lights to extend the number of daylight hours. How could you use your results to help someone improve their production of tomatoes in a greenhouse?

The mechanism of photosynthesis

To demonstrate conclusively that photosynthesis occurs only in the **chloroplasts**, we need to separate the chloroplasts from the rest of the cell. Hill managed to do this in 1937 and in 1954 Arnon proved that chloroplasts, separated from all other parts of the cell, can carry out the entire process of photosynthesis.

Photosynthesis is divided into two phases:

- **Light reaction** – chlorophyll absorbs light energy which is converted to chemical energy. Water molecules are split, oxygen is given off, and the hydrogen is used to react with carbon dioxide in the second phase. This phase needs light but is not affected by temperature.
- **Dark reaction** (this does not require light) – carbon dioxide is converted into sugars by a series of reactions. This phase, because it is made up of chemical reactions, is affected by temperature; the light reaction is not. An increase in temperature of 10 °C will approximately double the rate of a chemical reaction.

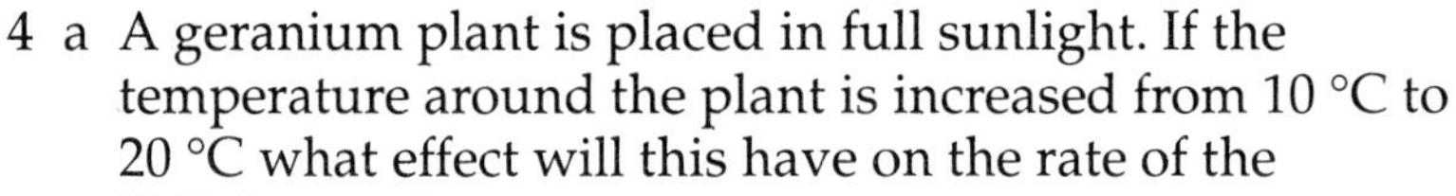

4 a A geranium plant is placed in full sunlight. If the temperature around the plant is increased from 10 °C to 20 °C what effect will this have on the rate of the
(i) light reaction
(ii) dark reaction?

b Another plant in full sunlight has the temperature around it reduced from 25 °C to 15 °C. What effect will this have on the rate of the
(i) light reaction
(ii) dark reaction?

The rate of photosynthesis

This depends on several factors but the four main environmental ones are the following, in order of priority:

a the light intensity falling on the plant
b the temperature, which affects the dark reaction. The optimum temperature is about 30 °C
c the amount of carbon dioxide in the atmosphere (usually 0.04 %)

d the amount of water available to the plant, but this only becomes important during severe drought conditions.

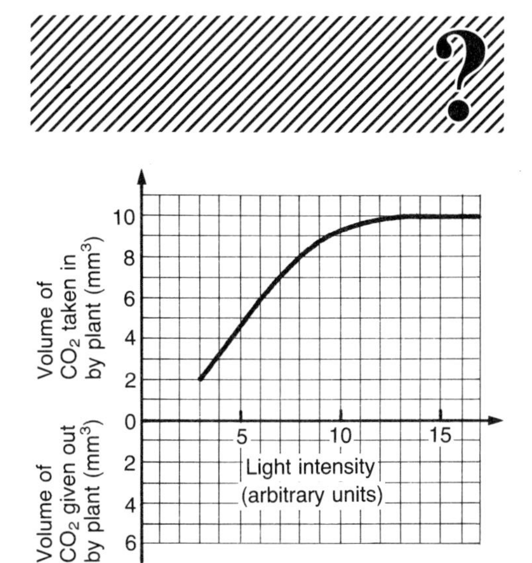

1.2 Graph showing the effect of different light intensities on the carbon dioxide exchange of a plant.

5 Fig 1.2 shows the effect of increasing the light intensity on the uptake of carbon dioxide by a green plant.

a How many units of light was the plant receiving when it took in 6 mm^3 of carbon dioxide?

b What increase in carbon dioxide uptake is caused by increasing the light intensity from
(i) 3 units to 6 units
(ii) 10 units to 13 units?

c Use a ruler to help you work out the light intensity at which carbon dioxide would be neither taken in nor given out by the plant.

The limiting factors of photosynthesis

Any one of the four factors labelled a–d above may limit the rate at which a plant can photosynthesise, provided all other factors are in excess. In dull weather, light is often the limiting factor so the rate of photosynthesis can be increased by increasing the light available. In a sunny climate, lack of carbon dioxide may limit the rate.

Fig 1.3 shows the rate of photosynthesis for a series of different light intensities. The rate rises sharply and then flattens out at a maximum.

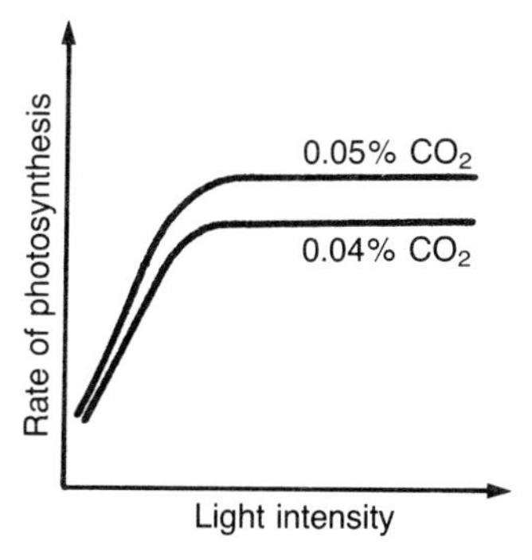

1.3 Graph showing the effect of different light intensities on the rate of photosynthesis at two different concentrations of carbon dioxide.

An increase in light intensity beyond this point does not increase the rate further. Some other factor, probably carbon dioxide or temperature, is acting as a limiting factor at this level of light intensity. Repeating the experiment with one factor altered (for example an increased level of carbon dioxide) may cause a further increase in the rate of photosynthesis. If it does, as in Fig 1.3, then the altered condition was previously the limiting factor.

6 Look at the graphs in Fig 1.4 which show the rate of photosynthesis under different conditions. At each plateau on the graphs, a factor is limiting photosynthesis.

Name the most likely limiting factor at points A, B, C and D on the graph.

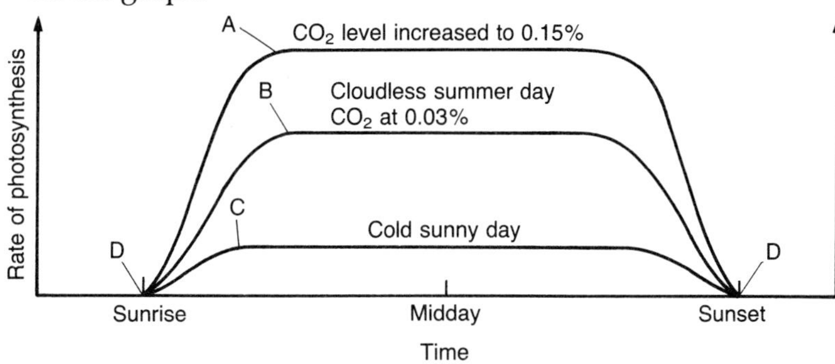

1.4 Graph showing the rate of photosynthesis at different times of the day under three different conditions.

7 The table below shows the rate of photosynthesis under eight different sets of conditions, A to H. Question parts a and b are worked examples to help you answer parts c and d.

	Temperature (°C)	Relative light intensity	CO_2 concentration (%)	Relative rate of photo-synthesis
A	20	3	0.04	75
B	20	6	0.04	75
C	20	3	0.14	150
D	20	6	0.14	195
E	30	3	0.04	75
F	30	6	0.04	75
G	30	3	0.14	180
H	30	6	0.14	270

a Which set of conditions gives the fastest rate of photosynthesis?
Answer: A temperature of 30 °C, light intensity of 6 units and a carbon dioxide concentration of 0.14 units, i.e. 'H'.

b What is the effect of
(i) increasing the temperature when there is plenty of light and carbon dioxide?
Answer: An increase in the rate of photosynthesis from 195 to 270 units.

(ii) increasing the light intensity when there is plenty of carbon dioxide and a high temperature?
Answer: An increase in the rate of photosynthesis from 180 to 270 units.

(iii) increasing the carbon dioxide concentration when there is plenty of light and a high temperature?
Answer: An increase in the rate of photosynthesis from 75 to 270 units.

c Explain why the rate of photosynthesis is the same in A, B, E and F.

d 0.04 % is the normal amount of carbon dioxide in the air. What do these results tell you about the benefits of adding carbon dioxide to the air?

Respiration

We have just seen that plants are able to convert light energy into chemical energy by photosynthesis. Plants store this chemical energy as foods such as starch or sugars and can provide this energy to all other forms of life. They are the producers that form the basis of all **food chains**.

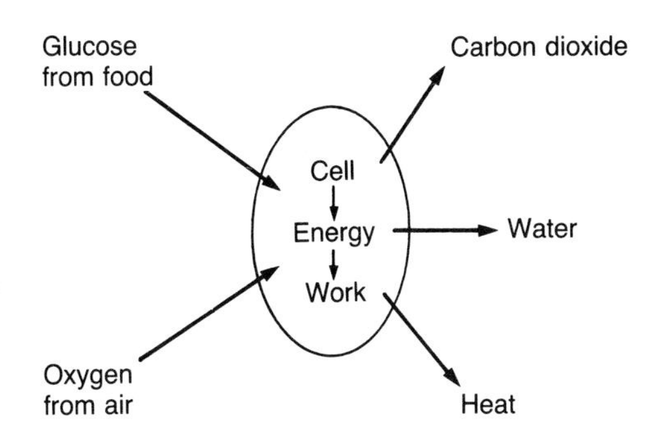

Raw materials **Waste products**

1.5 Exchanges carried out by a cell during respiration.

This energy cannot be used by plants or animals for any living process until it is released from the food molecules in which it is stored. The process which releases the energy from food is **respiration**.

All living organisms have to respire. There are two different ways in which they do this – **aerobic respiration** (using oxygen) and **anaerobic respiration** (without oxygen).

Aerobic respiration

This occurs in most organisms and requires a constant supply of oxygen. The raw materials enter the cell, respiration occurs and waste products are removed (Fig 1.5). It can be represented simply by the chemical equation that is the reverse of photosynthesis.

glucose + oxygen → carbon dioxide + water

This has an energy output of 2800 kJ/mol of glucose.

See if you can work out the balanced symbol equation for this reaction. **Hint:** look in the section above on photosynthesis.

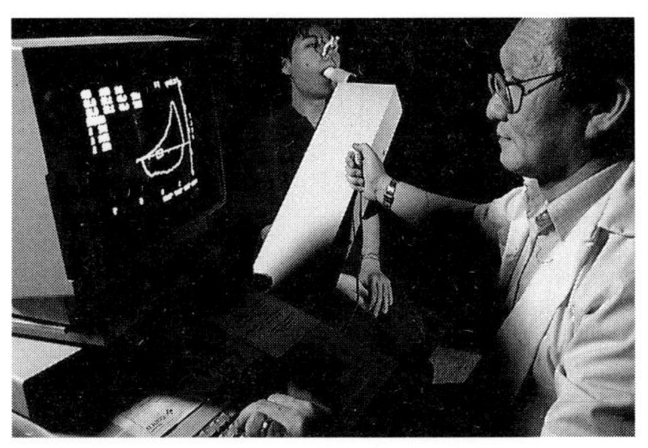

1.6 A spirometer

To respire aerobically, we need to **breathe** in order to take the necessary oxygen into our bodies and release the waste carbon dioxide (see Chapter 3). We can measure the volumes of air entering and leaving our lungs in each breath using a piece of apparatus called a spirometer – see Fig 1.6. A pen moves up and down on a revolving drum making a trace as the person breathes in and out. Fig 1.7 represents such a trace.

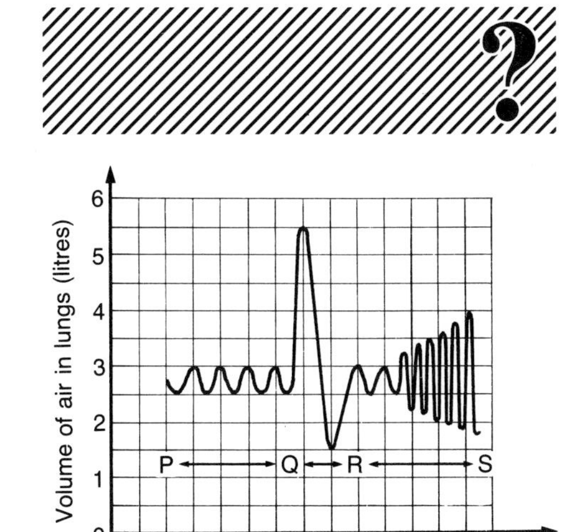

1.7 Spirometer trace of a subject starting at rest (P-Q).

8 a In which direction does the pen move when air is being
(i) inhaled
(ii) exhaled?

b What volume of air is inhaled and exhaled at each breath during period P–Q when the person is at rest?

c Describe in detail the breathing pattern of the subject during period Q–R on the graph.

d Work out the maximum amount of air that this person can exhale in one breath as indicated by the graph.

e What is the person likely to be doing to cause the graph to change during period R–S on the graph?

Worked example

An experiment was set up, as shown in Fig 1.8, to find the volume of oxygen absorbed during aerobic respiration by germinating pea seeds.

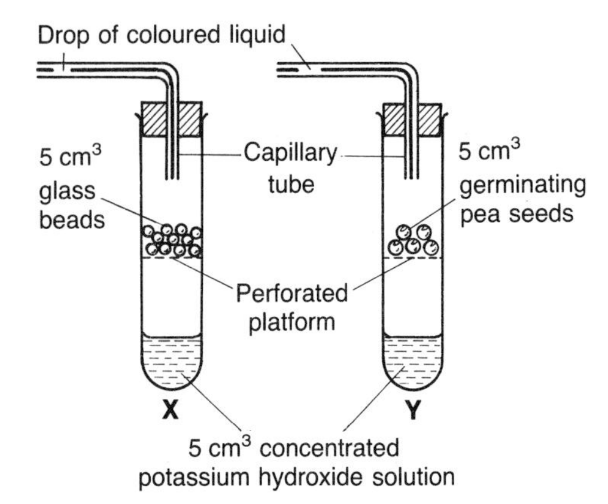

1.8 Apparatus used to find the volume of oxygen absorbed during aerobic respiration by germinating pea seeds.

In X and Y, the volumes of the test tubes were the same. The cross-sectional area of each capillary tube was 2 mm^2. The weight of the seeds was 10 g. The experiment was carried out at 20 °C in uniform light and constant atmospheric pressure.

After one hour the drop of coloured liquid in the capillary tube X had not moved. In Y the drop in the capillary tube had moved 40 mm from its position at the start of the experiment in the direction of the test tube.

a What must have caused the movement of the drop in capillary tube Y?

Answer: The seeds respired and exchanged oxygen for carbon dioxide. The carbon dioxide was absorbed by the potassium hydroxide solution so that the coloured liquid in the capillary tube was drawn into tube Y.

b Why do you think perforated platforms were used?

Answer: To allow gas movement throughout each tube.

c Why do you think 5 cm^3 of glass beads were placed in tube X?

Answer: These beads occupied the same amount of space in tube X as the seeds in tube Y, so that both tubes contained the same amount of air at the beginning of the experiment.

d Work out

(i) the volume of oxygen (in mm^3) which the seeds used in one hour.

Answer: The volume of oxygen absorbed is equal to the volume of the capillary tube along which the coloured liquid moved. This is 40 mm $\times$ 2 mm^2 = 80 mm^3.

(ii) the volume of oxygen absorbed per gram of seed.

Answer: 80 mm^3 of oxygen was used by 10 g of seed, so 80/10 = 8 mm^3 of oxygen was used per gram of seed.

e What would you expect to happen to the rate of oxygen uptake by the seeds if the experiment were carried out

(i) at 10 °C in uniform light?

Answer: Respiration would be slower at this lower temperature so the liquid in capillary tube Y would move more slowly. (Since respiration is a series of chemical reactions, the reduction in temperature of 10 °C would have approximately halved the respiration rate.)

(ii) at 20 °C in the dark?

Answer: There is no change in temperature and respiration would go on at the same rate in the dark as in the light. (Respiration is not affected by light/dark conditions.)

9 The apparatus in Fig 1.9 was used to investigate the composition of a bubble of air (exhaled) after exercise. With the bubble always at constant temperature and pressure, the following results were obtained:

Length of gas bubble in contact with water = 100 mm

Length of bubble after contact with potassium hydroxide (which removes carbon dioxide) = 95 mm

Length of bubble after contact with potassium pyrogallol (which removes oxygen) = 80 mm

a Work out the percentage of carbon dioxide present in the original bubble.

b Work out the percentage of oxygen present in the original bubble.

c Use a text book (in a library search) to find out how these percentages compare with the amounts of carbon dioxide and oxygen in the atmosphere.

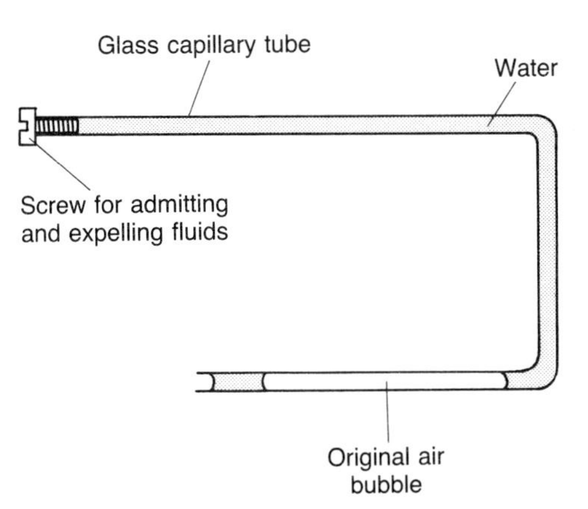

1.9 Apparatus used to investigate the composition of a bubble of exhaled air.

The storage of energy in the cell

Inside the many **mitochondria** in a cell, enzymes break down the glucose molecules in a series of stages. Each stage is controlled by a different enzyme and a small amount of the total energy of the molecule is released.

Glucose
enzyme 1 ↓
Substance B + energy
enzyme 2 ↓
Substance C + energy
several more stages ↓
Carbon dioxide + water
(Total energy output = 2800 kJ/mol of glucose)

In the mitochondria of each cell this energy is used to make molecules of the energy-rich compound called **adenosine triphosphate (ATP)** as follows:

$$\text{adenosine diphosphate (ADP)} + \text{phosphate} \xrightarrow{\text{energy from respiration}} \text{adenosine triphosphate (ATP)}$$

$$A - Ⓟ - Ⓟ \quad + \quad Ⓟ \quad \rightarrow \quad A - Ⓟ - Ⓟ \sim Ⓟ$$

(where Ⓟ = phosphate group)

ATP is the intermediate energy compound in the cell. If the energy in the glucose molecules were released suddenly, the cell would be destroyed by the excess heat. When released slowly, via ATP, most of the energy can be harnessed for the work of the cell.

The chemical bond Ⓟ ~ Ⓟ is 'energy-rich' and when broken down provides energy for the work of the cell:

ATP → ADP + Ⓟ + energy for work

The amount of energy released by an organism in a given time is known as its **metabolic rate**. Whenever energy is transferred from one compound to another or used in work, some is lost as heat energy. This is usually considered as lost or wasted energy but warm-blooded animals, such as mammals, can control their heat loss and use it to maintain a constant body temperature.

Surface area to volume ratio

The surface area to volume ratio of an animal is important in determining how quickly it will lose heat from its body. Animals with large surface area to volume ratios will lose their body heat faster than animals with smaller surface area to volume ratios.

10 The table below, when completed, shows the relationship between surface area and volume in a series of cubes of different sizes (Fig 1.10).

Length of side of cube (cm)	Total surface area (cm^2)	Volume (cm^3)	Surface area/ volume ratio
1	6	1	6:1
2	?	?	?
3	?	?	?

a Copy out the table, inserting the correct figures in the places marked '?'.

b What happens to the surface area to volume ratio as the cubes increase in size?

c The African elephant, which lives in a hot climate

- has almost hairless skin
- can increase its surface area by approximately one-sixth by raising its large ears.

How do you think each of these facts helps the elephant to control its body temperature?

d An adder is said to be 'cold-blooded' whilst mammals are 'warm-blooded'. Use a reference book to help you answer the following questions.

(i) Explain what is meant by the term 'warm-blooded'.

(ii) Explain two ways in which being 'warm-blooded' has advantages over being 'cold-blooded'.

(iii) Apart from mammals, name one other animal group (phylum) that is 'warm-blooded'.

1 cm
1 cm
1 cm

Area of face = 1 × 1 = 1 cm^2
Total area = 6 × 1 = 6 cm^2
Volume = 1 × 1 × 1 = 1 cm^3

1.10 Areas and volume of a cube.

Anaerobic respiration

The breakdown of glucose *without* oxygen occurs in some fungi and bacteria, and also in muscles during vigorous exercise. It is not as efficient as aerobic respiration in terms of energy production and ATP yield.

Anaerobic respiration in yeast (fermentation)

This process is important in the baking and brewing industries. Single-celled yeasts grow and divide very rapidly and obtain their energy by breaking down sugars as shown below:

glucose → ethanol + carbon dioxide

$C_6H_{12}O_6 \rightarrow 2\,C_2H_5OH + 2\,CO_2 + \text{energy}$

Energy output = 200 kJ/mol of glucose

Ethanol and carbon dioxide are the waste products. Carbon dioxide is used to make dough rise and the alcohol produced by brewer's yeast is used in beer- and wine-making.

'Gasohol'

Sugar cane is a fast-growing tropical plant. The sugar it provides can be fermented to make alcohol. Alcohol can be used instead of petrol in cars. It can be mixed with petrol to produce 'gasohol'.

After the sugar cane has been crushed to remove the sugar, a woody material called bagasse is left. This can be used as a solid fuel to provide heat for the distillation of the fermented sugar.

In Brazil many cars now run on alcohol fuel made in this way and Brazil has plans to eventually replace all petrol by alcohol.

1.11 Garage selling alcohol in Brazil.

Anaerobic respiration in muscle

1.12 A runner after a race.

During vigorous exercise the oxygen supply to the cells becomes insufficient despite faster breathing. Anaerobic respiration occurs at the same time as aerobic and supplies extra energy for muscle contraction. Lactic acid accumulates and an **oxygen debt** is built up.

glucose → lactic acid + energy

The lactic acid enters the bloodstream and passes to the liver where it can be broken down to other substances. The reactions that get rid of the lactic acid use up oxygen, and this makes up the 'oxygen debt' which now has to be repaid.

11 a When do our muscles respire anaerobically?
b Explain why this cannot go on indefinitely.
c Why do the following animals need to respire anaerobically for long periods of time?
(i) tapeworms (ii) seals (iii) mud-burrowing worms

Gas exchange by plants

The overall exchange of gas between plants and the atmosphere depends on the light conditions.

During daylight, plants carry out photosynthesis and respiration. The rate of photosynthesis is much greater than the rate of respiration and supplies all the oxygen for energy release. It also uses up the waste carbon dioxide from respiration. During daylight, gas exchange with the environment involves the overall uptake of carbon dioxide and release of oxygen.

Note All plants and animals respire at all times. Green plants photosynthesise during daylight hours only.

During darkness plants carry out respiration only. They then take up oxygen and release carbon dioxide.

The compensation point

At two points every 24 hours, gas exchange through the tiny holes in the leaf surface, called **stomata**, seems to stop. These are the **compensation points** and they are the times at which the rates of photosynthesis and respiration are equal (see Fig 1.13).

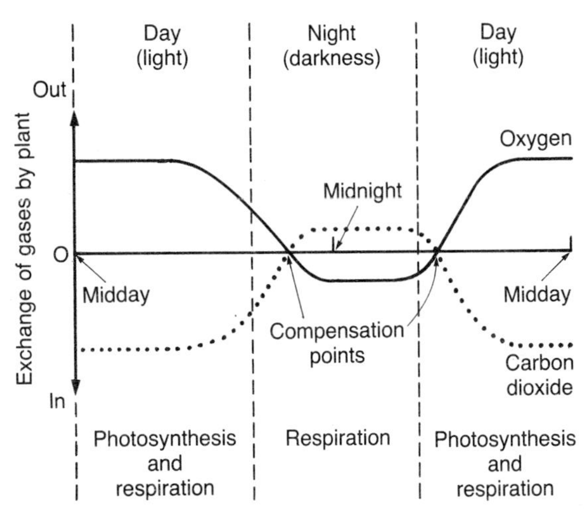

1.13 Exchange of oxygen and carbon dioxide by a plant over a 24-hour period.

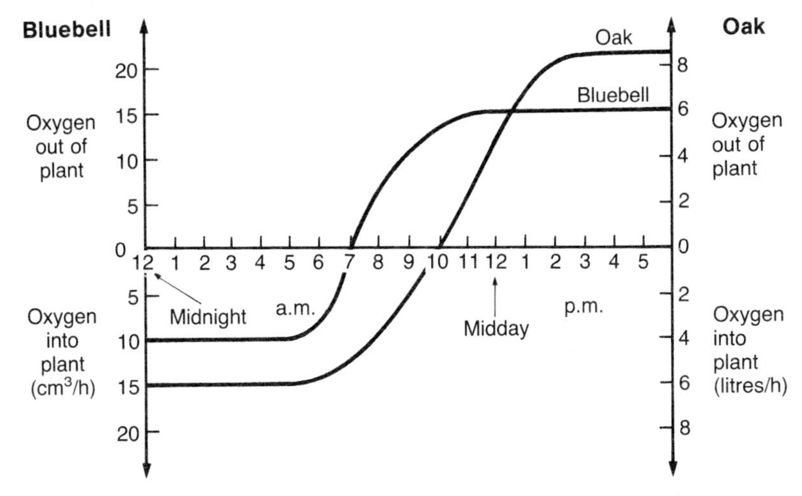

1.14 Effect of changing light intensities during the day on the rate of oxygen exchange by an oak tree and a bluebell.

12 Fig 1.14 shows the effect of increasing light intensity during the day on the gas exchange of two woodland plants – an oak tree which has a leaf canopy in full sunlight and a bluebell which lives in the shade of the oak tree.

a At which time of day is the compensation point achieved by the
(i) oak tree (ii) bluebell?

b Why do you think it is an advantage for the bluebell to reach its compensation point at a lower light intensity than the oak tree?

c Why do you think the graph for the oak tree reaches a higher plateau than the graph for the bluebell?

d How much oxygen does the bluebell require for respiration between 2 a.m. and 3 a.m?

e How much oxygen does the bluebell produce by photosynthesis between 2 p.m. and 3 p.m?

Answers

1 Producer: thistle; consumers: dog, blackbird, kangaroo.

2 a oxygen
 b photosynthesis (which produces the oxygen) only occurs in sunlight
 c water

3 a (i) Bacteria are around the chloroplast. (ii) Random small numbers around the *Spirogyra*.
 b Chloroplast. Aerobic bacteria are only around the chloroplast area which is in the light.
 c Only chloroplast in the light produces oxygen (and attracts the bacteria).
 d Use a prism as shown.

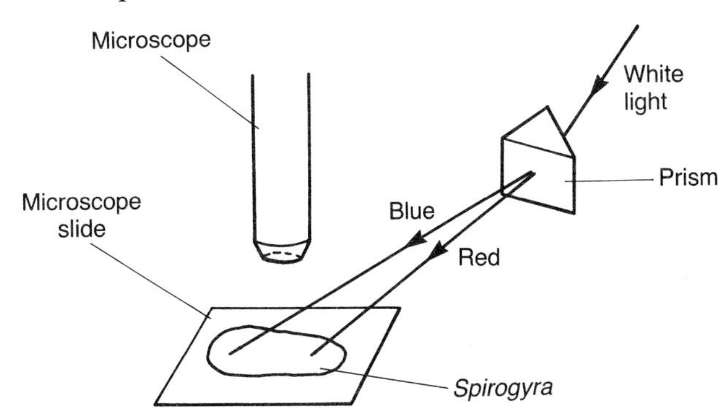

1.15 Experimental set-up to investigate the effect of different colours of light on photosynthesis.

(i) Count numbers of bacteria in different coloured areas of *Spirogyra*.
(ii) Use the colour of light which gives most photosynthesis.

4 a (i) no change
 (ii) rate roughly doubled
 b (i) no change
 (ii) rate roughly halved

5 a 6
 b (i) 2 to 6
 (ii) 9.5 to 10
 c 1 to 2

6 A CO_2 or sunlight; B CO_2; C low temperature; D sunlight

7 c lack of CO_2 – 0.04 %
 d More CO_2 results in more photosynthesis.

8 a (i) up
 (ii) down
 b 1 L
 c Deep inhalation followed by full expiration, then inspiration to full breathing.
 d 4 L
 e increasing exercise

9 a 5 %
 b 15 %
 c The atmosphere contains: O_2, approximately 21 %; CO_2, approximately 0.04 %

10 a

Length of side of cube (cm)	Total surface area (cm²)	Volume (cm³)	Surface area/ volume ratio
1	6	1	6:1
2	**24**	**8**	**3:1**
3	**54**	**27**	**2:1**

 b decreases
 c Each allows more heat to escape from the elephant's body.
 d (i) Animal maintains a constant warm temperature irrespective of the environment.
 (ii) Animal can be more active on cold days and it can live in colder climates.
 (iii) birds

11 a During vigorous exercise when there would be a shortage of oxygen in the muscles.
 b Poisonous lactic acid builds up (causing cramp).
 c (i) In the gut, where the tapeworm lives, there is little oxygen.
 (ii) There is no oxygen available during a deep dive.
 (iii) There is little oxygen available in the mud.

12 a (i) 10.00 a.m; (ii) 7.00 a.m.
 b The bluebell grows in the shade of the oak at a lower light intensity. It must photosynthesise more efficiently at these lower light intensities.
 c The oak receives a higher light intensity and can photosynthesise more than the bluebell.
 d 10 cm^3
 e 20 + 10 cm^3 = 30 cm^3 (the extra 10 cm^3 oxygen allows for that used for respiration)

Chapter 2 Food chains

Starting points 

Do you understand the following terms: **producer, consumer, decomposer, ecosystem**? Write one or two sentences (no more) to explain what you understand by each term. Then check them against the glossary at the back of the book.

The 'non-living' environment supports living organisms. It therefore governs where they live and how many there are of them. Energy is needed for the constant recycling of materials within an **ecosystem**. It is lost as it flows through the ecosystem and must be replaced by energy from the Sun.

We have seen in Chapter 1 that only green plants can use solar energy directly. They convert it into the chemical energy of sugars by photosynthesis. Plants are able to build up proteins, fats and vitamins from sugars. They are therefore called the **producers** of the ecosystem. All animals (**consumers**) obtain their energy for growth and metabolism from producers. These feeding relationships can be summarised as a **food chain** where each stage of the chain is known as a **trophic level**. Microbial consumers, which aid the decay of dead organisms at all levels, are called **decomposers**. The following diagram shows a typical food chain:

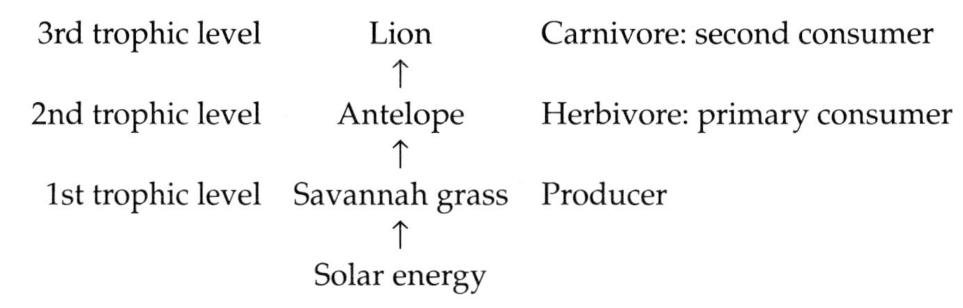

Only a small amount of the total energy that reaches the plant as light is incorporated into plant tissues. As energy is passed along the food chain there is a large loss between each level.

It is rare to find a simple food chain in an ecosystem. Usually there are several organisms at each level which may obtain food from any one of the lower levels. These complex feeding interrelationships are called **food webs**.

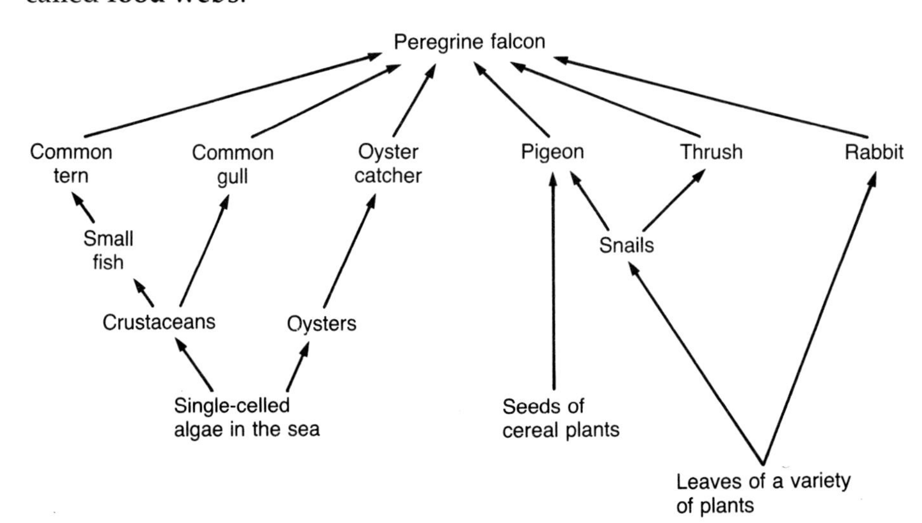

2.1 Food web for the peregrine falcon.

1 The food web in Fig 2.1 shows some of the feeding relationships of the peregrine falcon. It is a bird of prey which lives and nests on cliffs by the sea and feeds almost entirely on other birds.

a What is the ultimate source of energy for all the organisms in this food web?

b Name one organism from this food web which is a producer.

c What would happen to the common tern population if the numbers of common gulls were reduced?

d What would happen to the thrush population if the numbers of pigeons were increased?

e How is energy lost from each stage of this food web?

f During the 1960s the numbers of peregrine falcons in Britain declined. At this time cereal crops were often sprayed with insecticides such as DDT, Dieldrin and Aldrin. These substances can cause peregrine falcons to become infertile and also to lay thin-shelled eggs. Although the use of these insecticides is now restricted, large amounts of these chemicals have been washed into the oceans. With help from the food web shown above:

(i) Write out the food chain by which DDT sprayed onto a cereal crop could be passed to a peregrine falcon.

(ii) Suggest how the peregrine falcon received large doses of DDT even though each seed on the cereal plant carried only a small amount of the insecticide.

(iii) Suggest one way in which peregrine falcons could still be eating food containing DDT in the 1990s.

(iv) Unlike DDT which is a very stable chemical, more modern insecticides are **biodegradable**. Explain the meaning of the term 'biodegradable' and describe the advantage for the peregrine falcon of using such insecticides.

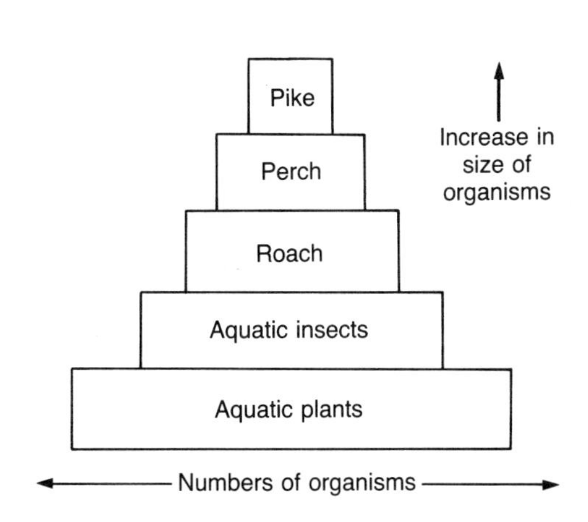

2.2 Pyramid of numbers for a food chain in a pond.

Pyramids of numbers

There is generally an increase in size (mass) of organism from primary consumer to the final carnivores in a food chain, but a decrease in numbers (see Fig 2.2). As there is a decrease in available energy at each successive link in the food chain there must also be a decrease in the amount of living material that it can sustain.

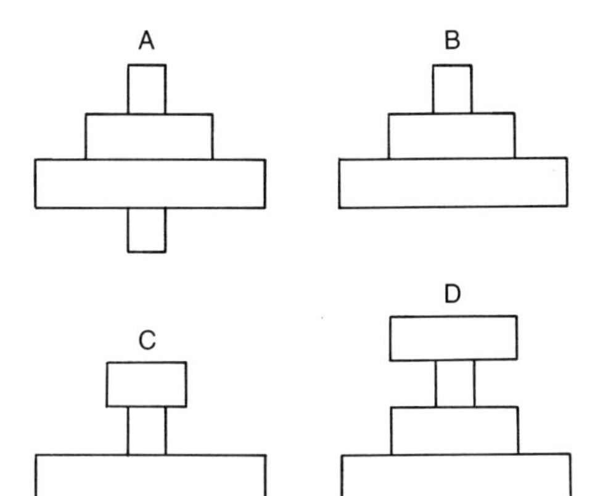

2.3 Different pyramids of numbers.

2 Fig 2.3 shows different patterns of pyramids of numbers for different food chains. The producers are shown as the bottom of each pyramid. The pyramids are not drawn to scale.

a Match each of the following food chains with one of the pyramids of numbers A – D.

(i) rose bush → greenfly → ladybirds → great tit
(ii) African savannah grass → wildebeest → lion
(iii) leaf litter → earthworms → hedgehog → fleas
(iv) waterhole vegetation → water buffalo → mosquitoes

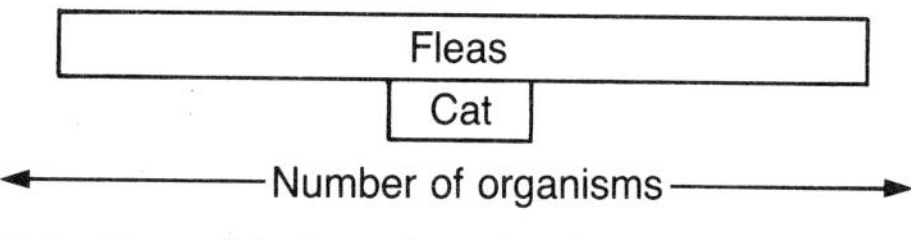

2.4 Pyramid of numbers for the cat → flea food chain.

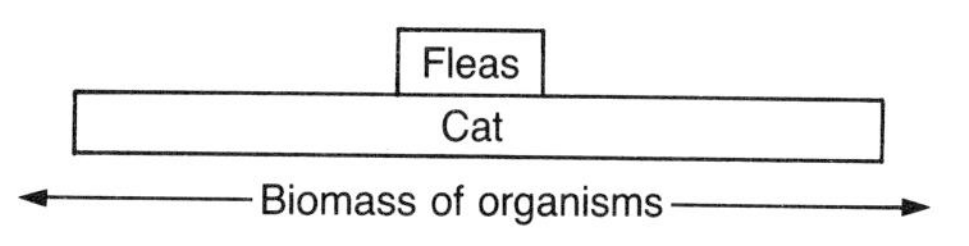

2.5 Pyramid of biomass for the cat → flea food chain.

Pyramids of biomass and energy

Some of the pyramids of numbers in question 2 are only pyramid shaped because we are counting just the *numbers* of organisms. Sometimes the pattern of numbers is reversed, for example, there may be around one hundred fleas feeding on the blood of one cat. A pyramid of numbers for this situation is shown in Fig 2.4.

However, if we measure the total mass of these two organisms we get a true pyramid pattern – a pyramid of **biomass** (the living weight of the organisms) as shown in Fig 2.5.

3 The following table shows an analysis of a pond ecosystem in Britain.

Trophic level	Organisms	Dry biomass (g/m^2)	Energy (kJ/m^2)
top carnivore	pike	0.3	18
secondary consumers	perch, roach	9.0	230
primary consumers	crustaceans, insects	41.0	670
producers	algae, aquatic plants	785.0	13 200

a Why is it better to use dry biomass as a measure rather than fresh biomass?

b For this pond ecosystem draw accurate scaled diagrams on graph paper to show
(i) a pyramid of biomass
(ii) a pyramid of energy.

Worked example

The amount of energy in each trophic level of a food chain decreases rapidly from the producers to the top carnivores. Below is some data on the energy budget for an agricultural field ecosystem. This shows how much energy each square metre of field received in one year, and what happened to the energy used by the grass in the field.

Total energy received from sunlight	1 000 000 $kJ/m^2/yr$.
Total energy gained by photosynthesis	50 000 $kJ/m^2/yr$.
Total energy lost through respiration	29 000 $kJ/m^2/yr$.

a Calculate the percentage of the sunlight energy received which is fixed by the grass in photosynthesis.

Answer $(50\,000/1\,000\,000) \times 100 = 5\ \%$.

b Calculate how much energy is used for new growth by the grass.

Answer The energy available for new growth will be the difference between the energy provided by photosynthesis and the energy used by respiration. This is 50 000 – 29 000 = 21 000 $kJ/m^2/yr$.

c Calculate the percentage of the energy fixed in photosynthesis which is used for new growth.

Answer The energy for new growth is 21 000 $kJ/m^2/yr$.
As a percentage of energy fixed by photosynthesis this is
$(21\,000/50\,000) \times 100 = 42\ \%$.

d Suggest what happens to the energy from sunlight which is received by the grass but is not used in photosynthesis.

Answer Much of the energy in sunlight is not light energy which can be used for photosynthesis. For example, the heat energy in the sunlight is not directly used for photosynthesis.

This pattern of only a small amount of the energy taken in by an organism being used for growth is repeated at each trophic level.

4 Here is some information about the energy available to a bullock feeding on the grass in the field referred to above.

Energy in grass eaten by the bullock	3050 $kJ/m^2/yr$.
Energy released in respiration	1020 $kJ/m^2/yr$.
Energy lost in faeces and urine	1900 $kJ/m^2/yr$.

a Work out the percentage of the available energy in the grass which is eaten by the bullock.

b Suggest why the bullock is only able to make use of such a low proportion of the available energy in the grass.

c What percentage of the energy actually taken in by the bullock is used for new growth?

d In terms of food efficiency, explain why the raising of bullocks in a field for meat produces so little food compared with using the field to grow vegetables.

e Why does our diet contain more meat from herbivores than from carnivores?

f In some tropical regions, native herbivores such as zebra, wildebeest and antelope yield more energy per unit area than introduced species of cattle. Suggest some reasons for this.

Variation in numbers within a population

Populations of organisms vary in response to changing conditions within an ecosystem, but over a long period of time the average size of each population remains the same.

If the predators become too numerous they will reduce the numbers of herbivores. Then the predator numbers will decline because of food shortage. Then, with fewer predators, the herbivore numbers will again begin to rise. Over a period of time there is a general balance in numbers of predator and prey. It is not an absolutely steady state and is often called a 'state of dynamic equilibrium' in the ecosystem.

5 Fig 2.6 shows the results from a study of the populations of two organisms, the weasel and its prey, the vole, in an enclosed farm area over a period of 12 years.

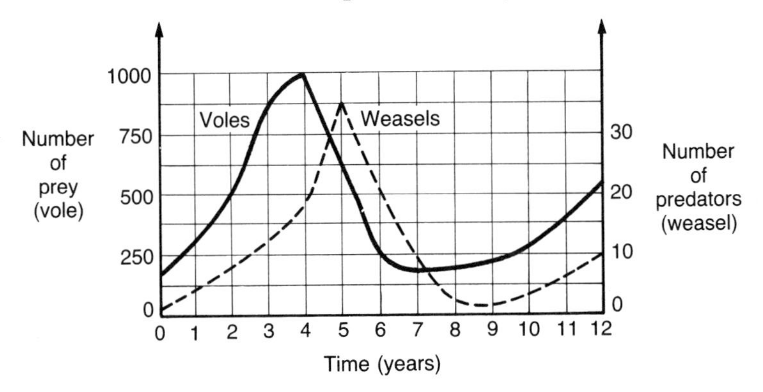

2.6 Graph showing population changes for weasels and voles over a 12-year period.

a How many years did the population of voles take to reach its maximum size?

b How many years did the population of weasels take to go from maximum to minimum numbers?

c How many times greater was the total number of weasels present in year 3 than the number present at the start of the study?

d Try to account for the decrease in voles and the increase in weasels during the period between year 4 and year 5.

Answers

1 a sunlight

b single-celled algae or cereal plant

c Increase due to more food from crustaceans.

d Decrease due to less food from snails.

e Each organism uses food (energy) for its own respiration so that this food energy cannot be passed on to the next organism in the food chain.

f (i) cereal plant → pigeon → peregrine falcon
(ii) A falcon may eat several pigeons which have eaten lots of contaminated seeds, therefore the DDT accumulates along the food chain.
(iii) Some DDT may have drained off farmland into the sea to contaminate the food chains from single-celled algae to falcon.
(iv) Biodegradable insecticides break down and would not accumulate along the food chains.

2 a (i) A; (ii) B; (iii) D; (iv) C

3 a Different tissues containing different amounts of water would produce inconsistencies.

b

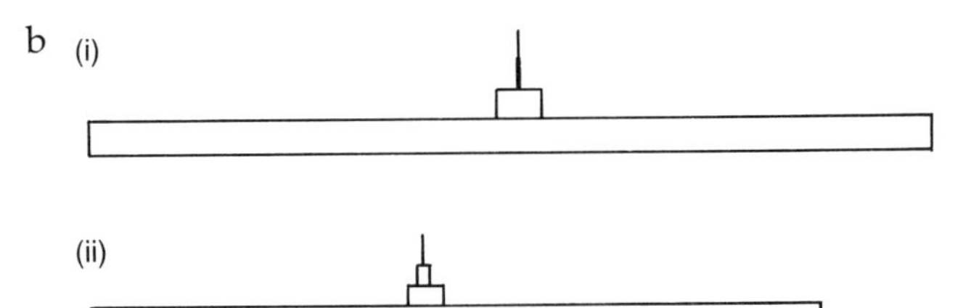

4 a $\frac{3050}{21\,000} \times 100 = 14.5\ \%$

b The bullock does not eat all the grass.

c $3050 - (1020 + 1090) = 940\ \text{kJ/m}^2\text{/yr}$

d Humans would eat vegetables directly. There is a greater loss of energy if bullocks are an intermediate in the food chain.

e If we eat carnivores, then the food chain becomes longer (than if we eat herbivores) and this causes a greater loss of energy.

f Native herbivores are likely to be better adapted to the local environment and therefore are likely to be more efficient in food production.

5 a 4 years b 4 years c 3 times

d Increasing number of weasels are eating more voles so the vole population decreases.

Chapter 3 Exchange

Starting points

Do you understand the following terms: **osmosis, turgid, plasmolysis, flaccid, semi-permeable membrane**? Write a sentence or two (no more) to explain what you think is meant by each term. Then check them in the glossary at the back of the book.

Pressures in cells

The cells, fluids and gases in plants and animals are constantly under pressure! Without it, plants would wilt, blood couldn't flow and vital organs like our kidneys would stop working. There are three main pressures that can affect living things:

- osmotic pressure from solutions that move through cell membranes in plants and animals – osmotic pressure is measured in terms of water potential which is explained overleaf
- hydrostatic pressure from blood that helps to regulate water levels and waste chemicals in the body
- air and gas pressures in and around the lungs that enable breathing and gas exchange to take place.

In this chapter we shall first examine **osmotic pressure**, the pressure due to water moving in and out of cells through their **semi-permeable membranes**.

Osmotic pressure

Work through the following question to remind yourself about osmosis.

1 Samples of raw turnip of equal mass are weighed, and soaked in a range of different sugar solutions and also in distilled water. After an hour, the turnip pieces are blotted dry, and reweighed. The table opposite shows the results.

a Work out the loss or gain in mass of the turnip sample in each liquid.

b Plot your results on a graph of loss or gain (vertically) against concentration of sugar (horizontally). Gains should go *above* the horizontal axis and losses *below*.

c At what concentration of sugar does no change in mass take place?

d What concentration of sugar is equal to the internal concentration of the turnip cells? How did you get your answer?

e What loss or gain in mass would occur if you soaked some turnip in
(i) 0.32 mol/L sugar solution
(ii) 0.85 mol/L sugar solution?
How did you get your answers?

Concentration of sugar (mol/L)	Original mass of turnip sample (g)	Final mass of turnip sample (g)
distilled water	8.5	13.3
0.1	8.5	13.0
0.2	8.5	11.6
0.3	8.5	9.5
0.4	8.5	9.1
0.5	8.5	8.6
0.6	8.5	8.0
0.7	8.5	7.7
0.8	8.5	6.3
0.9	8.5	5.2
1.0	8.5	5.1

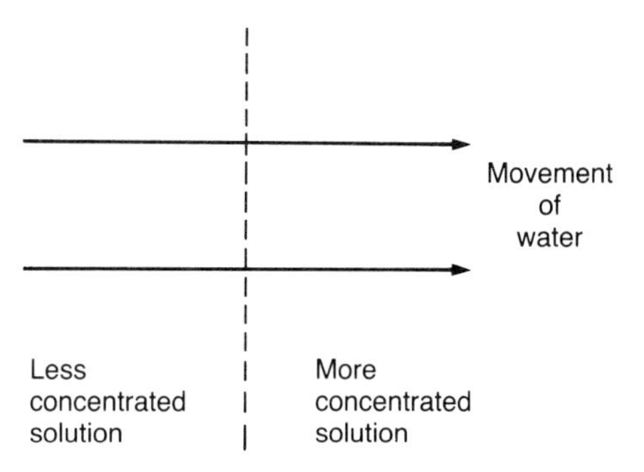

3.1 How water moves during osmosis.

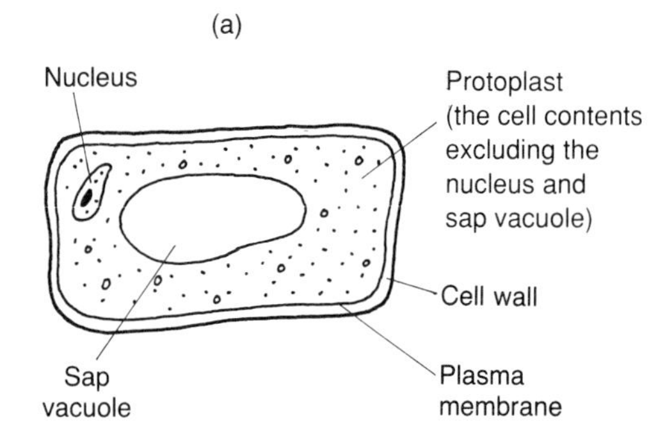

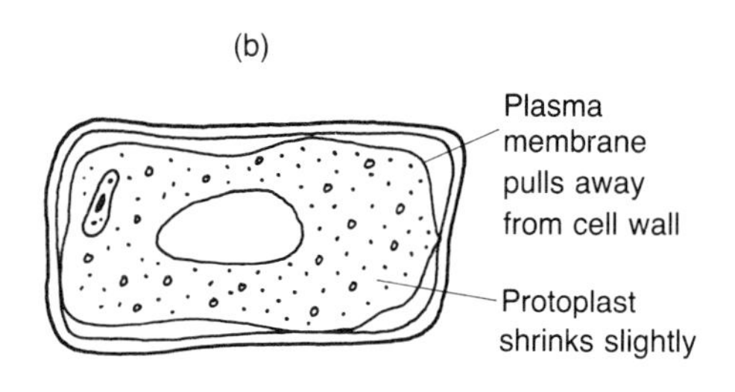

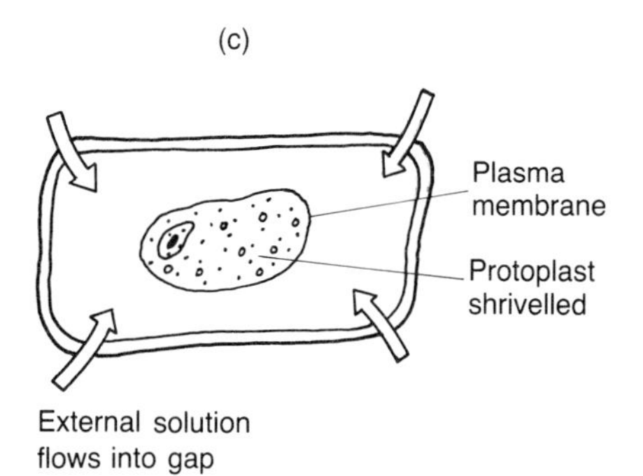

3.2 (a) Turgid cell, (b) cell in incipient plasmolysis surrounded by a solution of low solute potential and (c) fully plasmolysed cell in a solution of very low solute potential.

Note As animal cells do not have cell walls, there is no pressure potential and the equation for the water potential of an animal cell is simpler:
water potential = solute potential.

Water potential

Water is continuously moving in and out of cells through their semi-permeable membranes. 'Semi-permeable' means that small molecules such as water can pass through while larger particles such as starch cannot. The overall ability of any cell to lose or gain water until it reaches a balance point, or equilibrium, is called its **water potential**.

The water potential of a plant cell depends on two factors, the **solute potential** and the **pressure potential** as shown by the equation below:

water potential = solute potential + pressure potential

Let us look at each part of this equation in turn.

Solute potential

The solute potential depends only on the concentrations of the solutions inside and outside the cells. It predicts whether a solution will lose or gain water by osmosis. Look at Fig 3.1 which shows how water moves during osmosis.

Water will tend to flow from areas of high solute potential to low solute potential. The less concentrated a solution, the higher its solute potential as it is less likely to gain water. The more concentrated the solution, the more likely it is to gain water, and the lower its solute potential.

Pressure potential

This is a pressure that only develops when a plant cell is swollen with fluid, and the **cytoplasm** is pressing against the cell wall. The wall pushes back, and the difference between the two pressures can cause water to be squeezed out of the cell. This is the pressure potential.

Fig 3.2 shows how the pressure potential can disappear in a plant cell under different conditions.

Fig 3.2(a) shows a turgid cell. Imagine the cell being bathed in a concentrated sucrose solution with a lower solute potential than the solutions inside the cell. Water will flow out of the cell and it will become plasmolysed. The **protoplast** will start to pull away from the cell wall. This means that there cannot be any back pressure from the wall, and therefore no pressure potential. The cell is experiencing **incipient plasmolysis**, where water potential = solute potential. This condition is shown in Fig 3.2(b).

If this cell is now placed in an even stronger sucrose solution, so much water will leave the cell that the protoplast shrivels up. The cell is described as being **flaccid**. This is **full plasmolysis**, and nothing can stop the outside solution moving into the spaces left around the protoplast. Water potential still equals osmotic potential. This is shown in Fig 3.2(c).

2 Our body cells (and those of other animals) need to be bathed in **isotonic** solutions, whereas plant cells are normally surrounded by solutions of higher osmotic potentials. Try to explain this.

Calculations

Water potentials, solute potentials and pressure potentials in plant cells can be studied in a quantitative way by giving them numerical values.

$\Psi_{cell} = \Psi_p + \Psi_{s(int)}$

Ψ_{cell} = water potential of a cell

Ψ_p = pressure potential

$\Psi_{s(int)}$ = solute potential of a solution inside a cell

$\Psi_{s(ext)}$ = solute potential of a solution outside a cell

Ψ is the Greek letter 'psi'. All Ψ values are measured in the pressure units of megapascals or MPa.

The numbers used in water potential calculations

The numbers used for solute potentials may seem a little strange! Pure water has a Ψ_s value of zero. For solutions more concentrated than pure water, Ψ_s has *lower* (increasingly negative) values. Look at the chart below to see how this works.

	0.0	Ψ_s of pure water = highest Ψ_s possible
Ψs	−0.2	
(MPa)	−0.4	Ψ_s of a dilute solution = low Ψ_s
	−0.6	
	−0.8	Ψ_s of a concentrated solution = lower Ψ_s
	−1.0	
	−1.2	
	−1.4	Ψ_s of a more concentrated solution = lowest Ψ_s

Follow the worked example to check you understand this.

During osmosis, which way will water move for the following solution?

$\Psi_{s(ext)} = -0.8$ MPa | $\Psi_{s(int)} = -0.4$ MPa

A — Semi-permeable membrane — B

Water will move from the solution with the higher solute potential to the solution with the lower solute potential until there is a balance (or equilibrium). −0.4 is higher than −0.8, so water will move from B to A.

3 For each situation, work out which way the water moves.

	A	B
a	$\Psi_{s(ext)} = 0.0$ MPa	$\Psi_{s(int)} = -0.2$ MPa
b	$\Psi_{s(ext)} = -0.1$ MPa	$\Psi_{s(int)} = -0.6$ MPa

4 Remembering that solute potentials are related to concentration, complete these statements:
  a Osmosis is the movement of water through a semi-permeable membrane from a region of *high/low* solute potential to a region of *high/low* solute potential until there is an equilibrium.
  b A solution with a low concentration has a *high/low* solute potential.

Some useful facts

If $\Psi_{cell} = 0$ MPa, then the cell is fully turgid, and it cannot take in any more water.

If $\Psi_p = 0$ MPa, the cell is in incipient plasmolysis or is fully plasmolysed.

To recap:

$\Psi_{cell} = \Psi_p + \Psi_{s(int)}$

where Ψ_{cell} = water potential, Ψ_p = pressure potential and $\Psi_{s(int)}$ = solute potential of the cell's internal solution.

Follow through these two worked examples of water potential problems, then try the questions.

1 A cell has the following Ψ values: $\Psi_{s(int)} = -0.8$ MPa, $\Psi_p = 0.1$ MPa. It is placed in salt solution of $\Psi_{s(ext)} = -0.5$ MPa.
  a What is the original Ψ_{cell}?
  b Will the cell lose or gain water? Explain your answer.
  c What will be the new values for Ψ_{cell} and Ψ_p?

Answer

a
$$\Psi_{cell} = \Psi_p + \Psi_{s(int)} = 0.1 - 0.8 = -0.7 \text{ MPa}$$

b The cell has a water potential of -0.7 MPa, which is lower (more negative) than the solute potential of the external solution. Remember that water moves from the area of higher solute potential to the area of lower solute potential. So the cell gains water by osmosis, becoming more turgid until an equilibrium is reached.

c At this equilibrium, the tendency for the cell to gain or lose water is equal to the tendency for the outside solution to gain or lose water:

$\Psi_{cell} = \Psi_{s(ext)}$

So the new $\Psi_{cell} = -0.5$ MPa.

$\Psi_{cell} = \Psi_p + \Psi_{s(int)}$

$-0.5 = \Psi_p - 0.8$

$\Psi_p = 0.3$ MPa

2 A cell has $\Psi_{cell} = -0.5$ MPa, and $\Psi_{s(int)} = -1.0$ MPa. It is placed in a solution $\Psi_{s(ext)} = -1.0$ MPa.

a Calculate the original Ψ_p.

b Describe what will happen to the cell when it is placed in the external solution and calculate the new Ψ_{cell} and Ψ_p.

Answer

a $\Psi_{cell} = \Psi_p + \Psi_{s(int)}$

$-0.5 = \Psi_p - 1.0$

$\Psi_p = 0.5$ MPa

b The solute potential of the external solution is −1.0 MPa. The water potential of the cell is higher (less negative) than this at −0.5 MPa. Water will move out of the cell until equilibrium, and the cell will lose mass, become less turgid and decrease in pressure potential as the cell wall does not press back so hard against the cytoplasm.

At equilibrium, $\Psi_{cell} = \Psi_{s(ext)}$
so new $\Psi_{cell} = -1.0$ MPa.

$\Psi_{cell} = \Psi_p + \Psi_{s(int)}$

$-1.0 = \Psi_p - 1.0$

$\Psi_p = 0.0$ MPa

As the pressure potential is zero, this means the cell is flaccid and in either incipient plasmolysis or full plasmolysis.

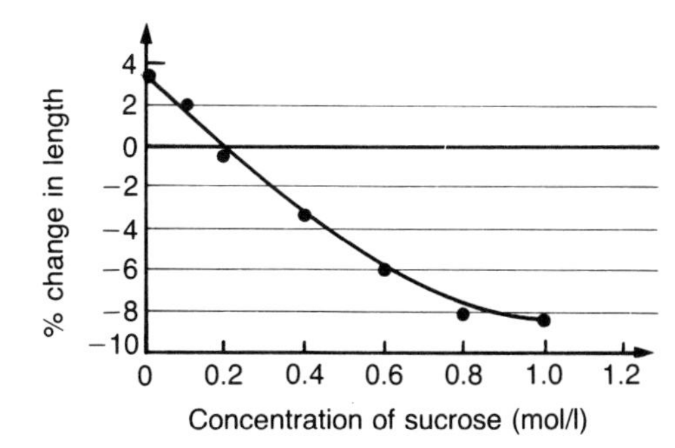

3.3 Graph showing the percentage change in length of potato pieces after soaking in different sugar solutions.

5 An experiment is carried out on osmosis using raw potato pieces of measured length. They are soaked in solutions of different sugar concentrations for an hour and the percentage changes in length are shown in Fig 3.3.

a At what concentration of sugar is there no change in mass? What does this represent?

b What is the value of Ψ_p at this point?

c One of the potato cells is shown in Fig 3.4, surrounded by its external solution.
(i) What is the Ψ_{cell}?
(ii) Will the cell lose or gain water? Explain your answer.
(iii) What will be the new Ψ_{cell}?

3.4 Potato cell surrounded by a sugar solution.

6 The table opposite gives the $\Psi_{s(int)}$ and Ψ_{cell} values for three beetroot cells.

Cell	Ψ_{cell} (MPa)	$\Psi_{s(int)}$ (MPa)
A	−0.3	−1.2
B	−0.4	−0.8
C	−0.7	−0.9

a Calculate the original Ψ_p for each cell.

b The cells are soaked in salt solutions of differing concentrations. The $\Psi_{s(ext)}$ for each solution is shown opposite.

For each cell state whether it will lose or gain water, and calculate the new Ψ_{cell}.

Cell	$\Psi_{s(ext)}$ (MPa)
A	−0.5
B	−0.8
C	0.0

3.5 Osmoregulation in an *Amoeba*

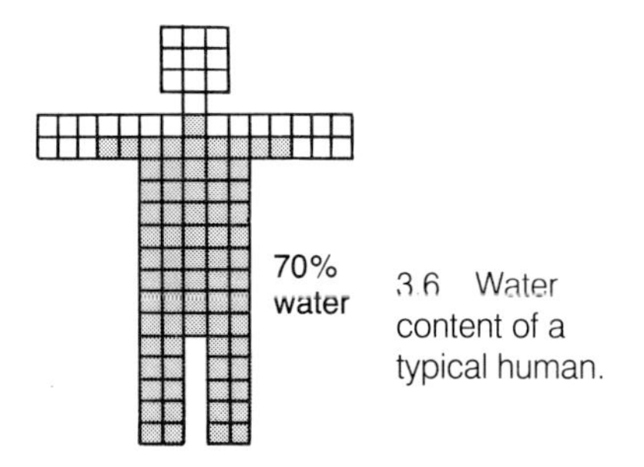

3.6 Water content of a typical human.

Osmoregulation

As animal cells do not have cell walls, their water potentials have no pressure potential component. The cells are more fragile than plant cells, so water and solutes need to be regulated carefully. This is called **osmoregulation**.

Single-celled freshwater organisms such as *Amoeba* and *Paramecium* experience a greater external osmotic potential than their own internal values. That is, their own internal concentration is greater than that of the freshwater in which they live. Being single-celled this poses a survival problem: water flows into their cells by osmosis and if this went unregulated the cell would burst. However, these organisms possess a mechanism for thriving in these conditions: they have one or more osmoregulatory **contractile vacuoles**. These rid the cell of excess water. Follow through Fig 3.5 showing how the contractile vacuole of an *Amoeba* works.

In more complex animals, most of the body is water. In humans, the blood and the fluids derived from blood that bathe our cells make up about 70 % of our bodies.

Osmoregulation in complex animals is not always just a matter of differences in osmotic and water potentials causing water to flow in and out of cells. A further factor is the **hydrostatic pressure** caused by the flow of blood through the various blood vessels.

Hydrostatic pressure

Blood circulates in our bodies under varying pressure from the pumping action of the heart. The blood travels in arteries, veins and capillaries that change in diameter and lumen. The elasticity of their walls causes more changes in pressure.

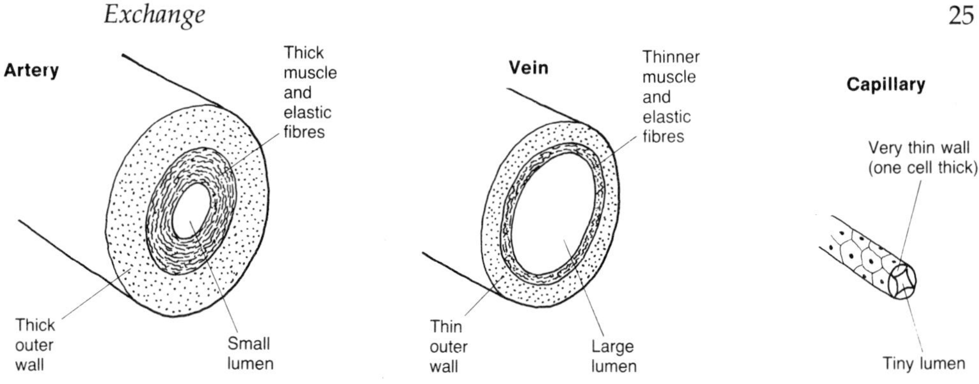

3.7 Cross-sections through an artery, a vein and a capillary.

7 Do you understand the connection between **blood**, **plasma** and **tissue fluid**? Write a brief description of what you think the connection is, and then check the glossary at the back of the book.

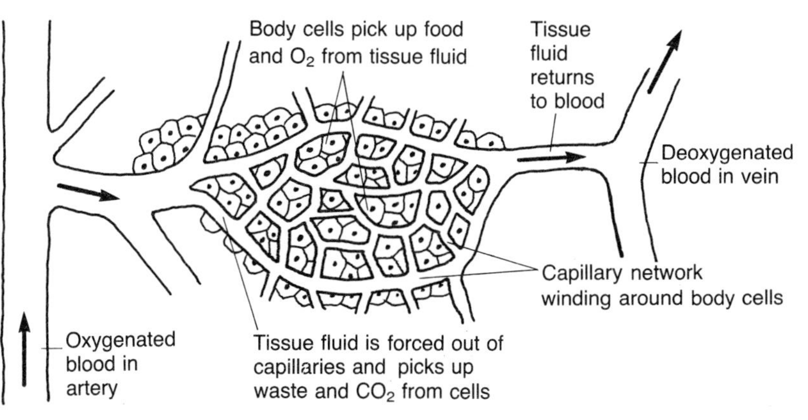

Although tissue fluid is mostly water, it does not leave the blood by osmosis. It is forced out under a pressure called a hydrostatic pressure, which is the pressure that develops when blood enters a capillary bed as in Fig 3.8.

3.8 A capillary bed.

8 Which part of the capillary bed has the greatest hydrostatic pressure?

As the tissue fluid bathes the body tissues, osmosis will occur to maintain the correct balance of water in the cells. (Nutrients and wastes will also diffuse in and out of the active cells.)

Remember that blood contains both water and dissolved solutes. This means there will be an overall water and osmotic potential in the blood opposing the hydrostatic pressure, and so drawing water back into the capillaries.

9 Where in a capillary bed will most fluid be returned? Briefly explain your answer.

Hydrostatic pressure in the kidneys

There is a particularly high hydrostatic pressure in blood entering the capillaries of the nephron, the working unit of the kidney. Fig 3.9 shows a diagram of a nephron.

10 What do you notice about the blood entering the glomerulus and the blood leaving it that contributes to this high pressure?

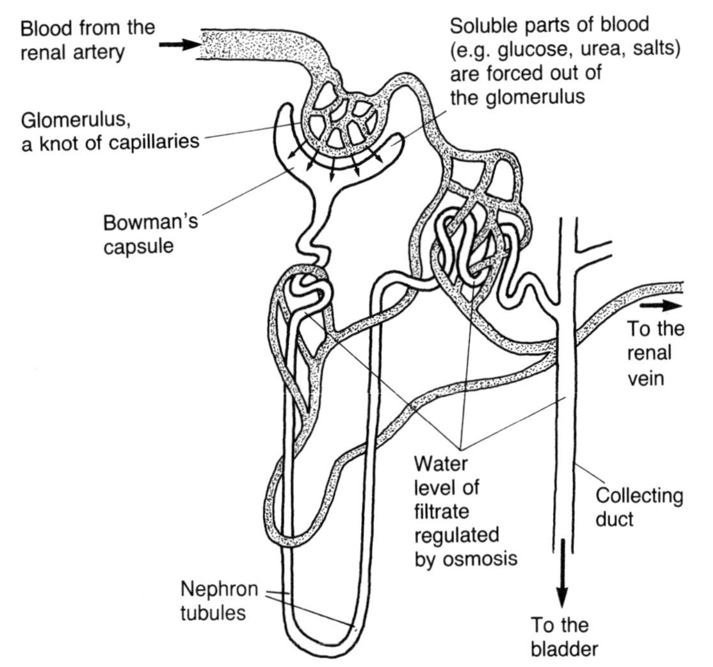

Because of the high hydrostatic pressure, water and the soluble parts of blood are forced out of the glomerulus capillaries into the body of the nephron. This special filtration of blood by the kidneys is called **ultrafiltration**. After ultrafiltration, the resulting fluid or **filtrate** travels down the nephron. If the osmotic potential of the filtrate is too high because the blood was too dilute, the excess water is removed by osmosis. Toxic chemicals such as urea and creatinine remain in the nephron, and together with the correct amount of water eventually form urine.

So in the kidneys, hydrostatic pressure is necessary for both osmoregulation and excretion.

3.9 A nephron.

Gas pressures during breathing and oxygen uptake

Our cells constantly use oxygen for metabolism and give off carbon dioxide as waste. As fast as the oxygen is used the supply must be renewed, and the waste gas removed. This renewal and removal involves two main factors:

- the process of breathing in and out known as the **respiratory cycle**
- gas exchange in the lungs.

Both processes depend on differences in gas pressures.

11 a You should be able to recall the details of the structure of the lungs and the route air takes to get inside them. Place the following stages of that route in the correct order, starting with air inside.

air inside; bronchiole; alveolus; trachea; bronchus.

b Copy and complete the labelling of Fig 3.10.

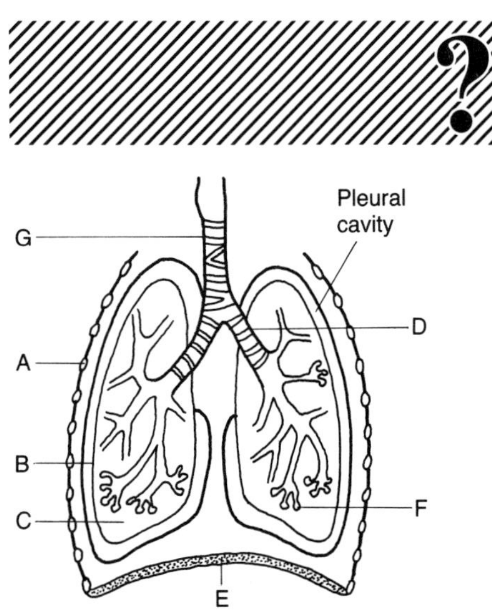

3.10 The chest cavity.

Pressures during the respiratory cycle

The important pressures inside the thorax during the respiratory cycle are those in the lungs and in the pleural cavity. Follow through the sequence of the respiratory cycle using Fig 3.11.

Immediately after breathing out (expiration), the thorax is at rest. Air pressure in the lungs is equal to atmospheric pressure – about

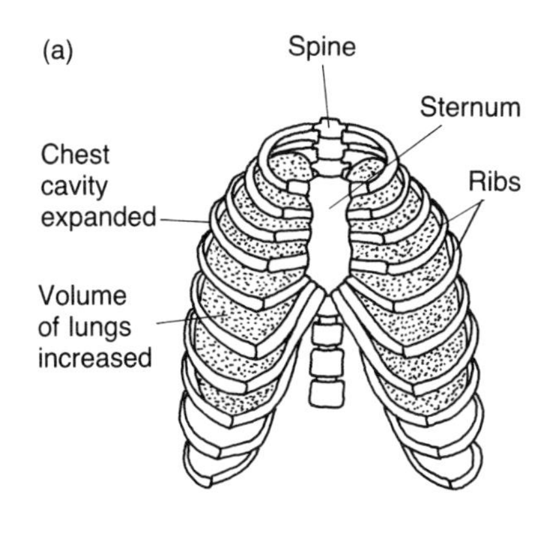

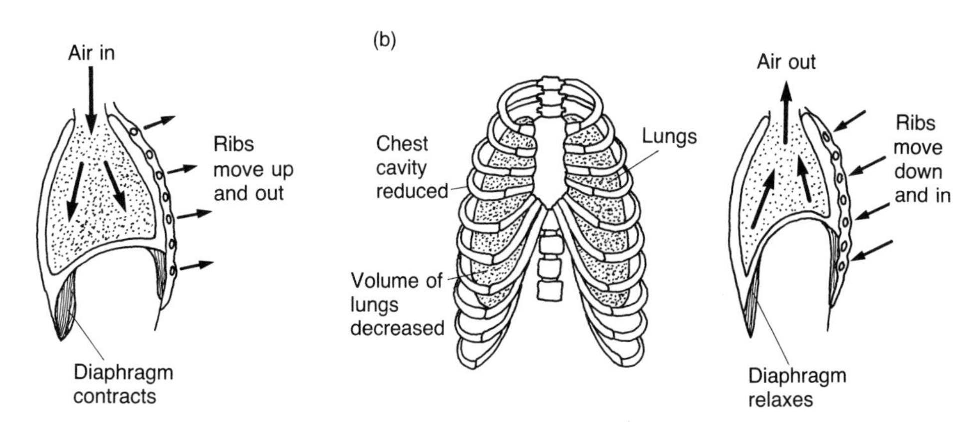

3.11 (a) Thorax during inspiration, (b) thorax during expiration.

100 kPa – although the pleural cavity pressure is slightly less. This is because the elastic, stretchy lung tissue pulls away a little from the walls of the thorax.

Fig 3.11(a) shows the thorax during inspiration (breathing in). The chest cavity has clearly expanded and this will lower the pleural cavity pressure further. Lung pressure drops to below atmospheric and air can rush in.

12 What effect will this have on the volume and pressure of the lungs?

Fig 3.11(b) shows the thorax after expiration. The ribs and diaphragm move down and press on the pleural cavity, so the pressure inside rises. This increases the pressure in the lungs, and together with the elastic recoil of the lungs forces air out.

The graph below (Fig 3.12) summarises the changes in pleural cavity and lung pressures in an adult.

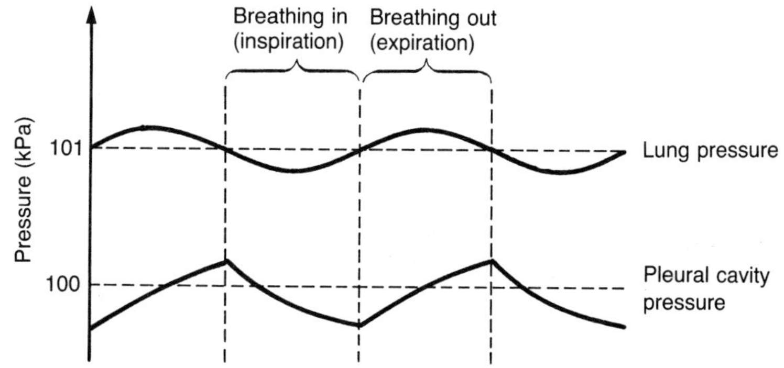

3.12 Graph showing changes in pleural cavity and lung pressures during the respiratory cycle.

Pressures during gas exchange

13 What do you understand by the term **diffusion**? Write a sentence explaining what it is, then check it in the glossary.

Gas exchange in the lungs occurs between the alveoli and the blood capillaries surrounding them (Fig 3.13).

14 Give three adaptations of an alveolus for the job of gas exchange.

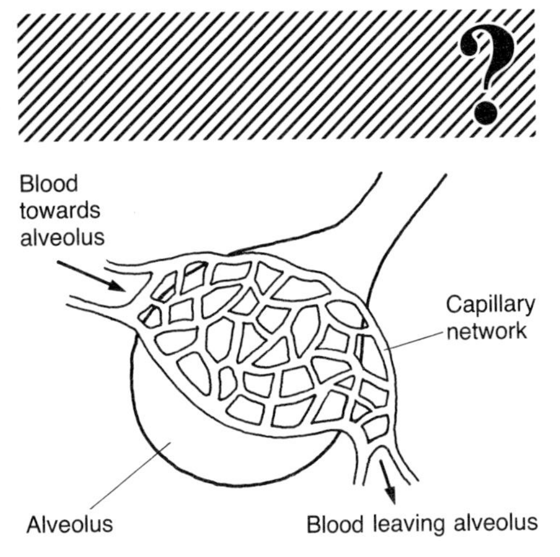

3.13 An alveolus and associated capillary network.

Partial pressures

Each gas that is part of a mixture of gases contributes to the total pressure of the mixture. The contribution is proportional to its percentage of the mixture. This contribution is called the **partial pressure** of the gas. For example normal air is a mixture of about 1/5 oxygen and 4/5 nitrogen and has a pressure of about 100 kPa. The partial pressure of oxygen is therefore 20 kPa and that of nitrogen 80 kPa.

15 Oxygen and carbon dioxide in blood going *to* the alveolus have different partial pressures from the ones they have in blood *leaving* the alveolus. Write a few sentences explaining why you think this is.

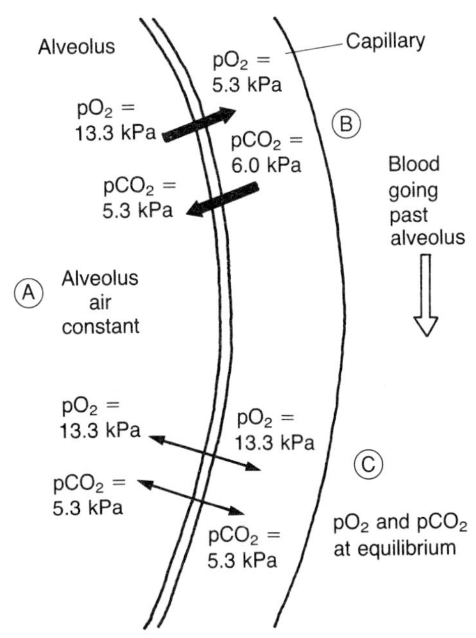

3.14 Gas exchange between an alveolus and a capillary.

Follow through Fig 3.14 which explains how the partial pressures of oxygen and carbon dioxide contribute to gas exchange.

At A Air in the alveolus has a partial pressure of oxygen, pO_2, of about 13.3 kPa and a pCO_2 of about 5.3 kPa. The partial pressures of gases in the alveoli stay more or less constant during gas exchange.

At B Blood arriving at the alveolus has a relatively low pO_2 as the oxygen has been used by respiring cells. However, the blood pCO_2 is higher than that in the alveolus as the cells have produced it as waste. Because of these gradients in partial pressure each gas diffuses from where its partial pressure is higher to where it is lower, until an equilibrium is reached between the blood gases and the alveolus gases.

At C The blood leaving the alveolus to go round the body has the same high pO_2 and relatively low pCO_2 as the air in the alveolus.

The table below compares typical percentages of carbon dioxide and oxygen in inspired and expired air of an adult.

	% CO_2	% O_2
Inspired air	0.03	20.95
Expired air	3.10	16.40

Answers

1 a + 4.8; +4.5; +3.1; +1.0; +0.6; +0.1; − 0.5; −0.8; − 2.2; −3.3; − 3.4

b

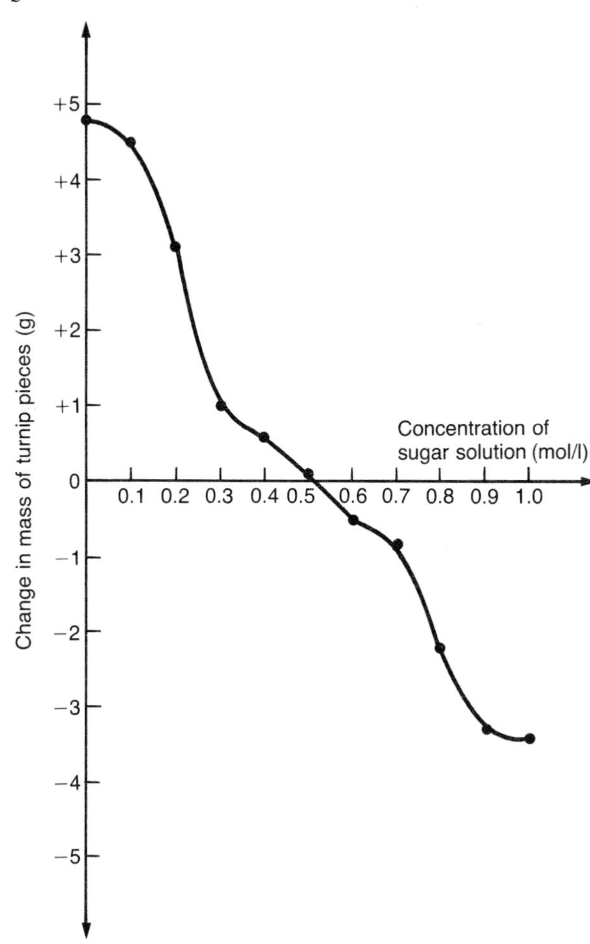

3.15 Change in mass of turnip pieces on soaking in different sugar solutions.

c approx. 0.52 mol/L

d Same answer as c. When the internal and external concentrations are equal, no osmosis takes place.

e (i) An increase in mass of approx. 0.9 g.

(ii) A decrease in mass of approx. 2.7 g – by reading from the graph.

2 Plant cells have a pressure potential (caused by their cell walls), which can force water out of the cell, in opposition to osmotic pressure trying to force water in. Animal cells do not have this and would burst if not bathed in an isotonic solution or if they did not have some mechanism to regulate their water content.

3 a from A to B

b from A to B

4 a from high to low

b high

5 a 0.2 mol/L

b 0.0 MPa

c (i) −0.7 MPa

(ii) The cell will lose water as Ψ_{cell} is greater than $\Psi_{s(ext)}$.

(iii) −0.5 MPa

6 a A 0.9 MPa; B 0.4 MPa; C 0.2 MPa

b A loses water, Ψ_{cell} = − 0.5 MPa; B loses water, Ψ_{cell} = −0.8 MPa; C gains water, Ψ_{cell} = 0.0 MPa.

7 See glossary.

8 The end nearest the artery.

9 At the end nearest the vein. The hydrostatic pressure here is lowest and the opposing osmotic pressure is highest. This tends to draw fluid back into the capillaries.

10 The blood enters the glomerulus in a wider vessel than the one by which it leaves it.

11 a air inside; trachea; bronchus; bronchiole; alveolus.

b A = rib, B = pleural membrane, C = lung, D = bronchus, E = diaphragm, F = alveolus, G = trachea.

12 The volume of the lungs will increase and the pressure will decrease.

13 See glossary.

14 Large surface area to volume ratio, thin walls, good blood supply, moist surface.

15 Blood going to the alveolus has more CO_2 and less O_2 than blood leaving it. Blood going to the alveolus is carrying CO_2 produced by cell respiration which has used up most of the O_2.

Chapter 4 Control and coordination

Starting points

Do you understand the following terms: **receptor, organ system, nervous system, endocrine system**? Write a sentence or two (no more) to explain what you understand by each term and then check them against the glossary at the back of the book.

Responding to changes

An organism would die if it could not respond to changes inside it and around it. So the organism needs a method of communication between its sense organs (or **receptors**) which receive information and its **organ systems** which respond to it. This information is transmitted in two ways – through the **nervous** and **endocrine** systems.

The endocrine system and hormones

Did you know? The blood circulates around the body about twice every minute.

Hormones are chemical substances which act as messengers to bring about a change in an organ system. They are produced by **glands** (called endocrine glands) which are usually sited away from the places where their effect is to take place. They are carried in the bloodstream from these glands to the **target organ**. They do not have an immediate effect because the blood takes some time to transport them. Although hormones travel throughout the body in the blood, each one will only have an effect on a specific target organ.

The pituitary gland

The pituitary gland at the base of the brain controls the activity of most of the hormones and the glands which produce them. It is sometimes called the 'master' endocrine gland. The pituitary gland works with another structure in the brain, the **hypothalamus**, which helps to sense changes in the composition of the blood. Once a hormone has had the required effect on an organ, a second hormone may be released, which blocks (or inhibits) the effect of the first. This brings stability back to the organ system. For example, glucagon will raise the level of glucose in the blood whereas insulin will lower it.

Stimulus increased

Response increased

Stimulus decreased

Response decreased

4.1 Negative feedback.

Feedback

Feedback is the term given to the control mechanisms of hormones. The type which is normally involved is called **negative feedback** (Fig 4.1). This type of mechanism is very important in the maintenance of a balanced internal environment (**homeostasis**). It is illustrated in Figs 4.1 and 4.2.

Fig 4.2 shows the mechanism for maintaining a constant level of glucose in the blood. If there is a high level of blood glucose, then the pancreas secretes insulin into the bloodstream, which has the effect of lowering the blood glucose level. When the level of glucose has been reduced to a tolerable level, the insulin production is then stopped and it is only released again when the glucose level in the blood rises to a high level.

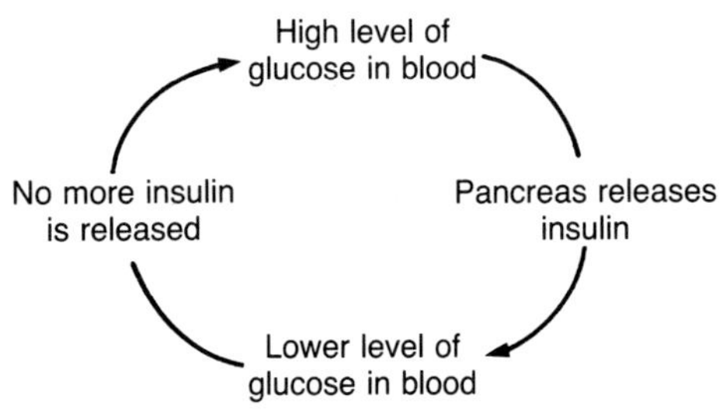

4.2 Control of glucose level in the blood.

Diabetes

Sufferers from the disease *diabetes mellitus* (usually called just diabetes) produce insufficient insulin which causes higher than normal levels of glucose in their blood. The symptoms include excessive thirst, production of large amounts of urine, hunger and blurred vision. Patients can go into a coma. The disease can be controlled by a suitable diet and/or by injections of insulin (Fig 4.3). Most patients can lead a normal life – indeed England soccer player Gary Mabbutt is a diabetic.

4.3 A diabetic injecting insulin.

1 When do you think the level of glucose in the bloodstream of a normal person rises?

2 The 'anti-diuretic hormone' (known as ADH for short), regulates the water content of the body tissues by preventing the kidneys from excreting water when the blood is too concentrated. The release of ADH, and therefore the control of osmotic pressure, is also a negative feedback mechanism. Draw a flow chart (similar to the one in Fig 4.2) for the release of ADH and the raising and lowering of the water level in the blood.

Positive feedback

The main mechanisms in homeo-static control systems are negative feedbacks. Positive feedback will only occur in homeostasis when the mechanisms leading to negative feedback break down. The result of this is that a small deviation from the norm leads to even more deviation and so on – with disastrous consequences.

Fig 4.4 summarises homeostatic control.

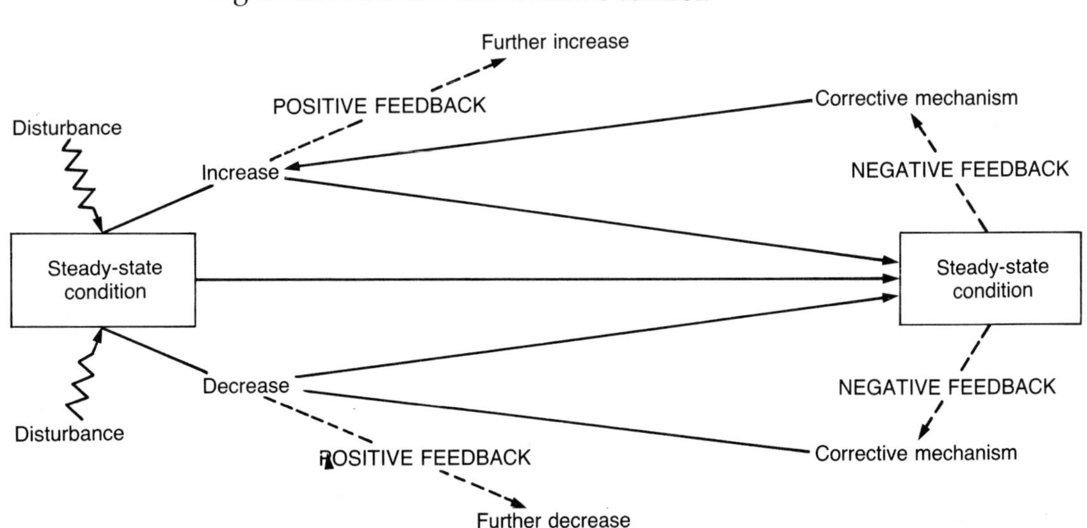

4.4 Homeostatic control.

The nervous system

A second method for communicating information around the body is the nervous system. Nerves transmit information in the form of electrical impulses. The table below compares the nervous system with the endocrine (hormonal) system.

Comparison between the nervous and endocrine systems.

	Type of communication	
	Nervous	**Hormonal**
Origin of stimulus	sense receptor	gland
Nature of stimulus	nerve impulse	hormone
Means of transmission	nerve fibre	blood
Destination of transmission	to a specific point	all points
Receptor	effector (muscle usually)	target organ
Speed of transmission	fast	slow
Effects	localised	widespread
Duration of effect	brief	long-lasting

As you can see from the table there are distinct differences between the two types of messengers (hormones and nervous impulses). The nervous system transmits information rapidly from one part of the body to another. This allows for an immediate response to the stimulus.

3 What do you understand by the terms **stimulus** and **response**? Write a sentence or two to explain what you understand by them then check them with the glossary at the back of the book.

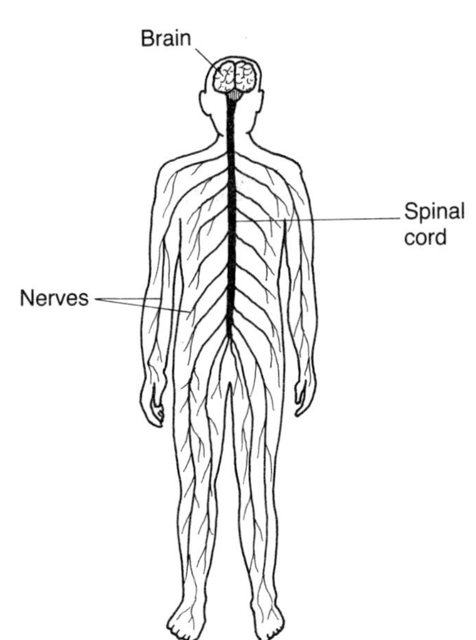

4.5 Brain, spinal cord and nerves.

Even simple organisms such as coelenterates (jellyfish, coral, sea-anemones) have a basic nervous system called a **nerve net**. However, we will concentrate on the nervous systems found in mammals.

The nervous system is made up of two main parts (Fig 4.5):

- the central nervous system (**CNS**)
- a series of nerves which link the CNS with the various organs.

The CNS itself is further divided into two parts:

- the brain
- the spinal cord.

Nerve impulses

Nerve impulses are tiny impulses of electricity that travel through the CNS and along the nerves.

Nerve cells

The nerve cells (or **neurones**) that make up the nervous system are grouped according to the function they carry out.

- Sensory neurones carry messages from the sense organs (receptors) to the spinal cord.
- The motor neurones carry messages from the spinal cord to a muscle or gland, called the **effector**, which carries out some action.
- Relay neurones are situated in the spinal cord and transmit the messages from the sensory neurones to the motor neurones.

All neurones have three main parts. These are:

- The cell body, which consists of a nucleus surrounded by cytoplasm.
- The axon, which is usually a long structure that carries the nerve impulses away from the cell body. The axon is surrounded by a fatty substance called the myelin sheath. The myelin sheath acts as an insulator which helps to keep the transmission of impulses fast.
- Dendrites, which are the nerve endings that obtain or pass on impulses from either sense cells or other neurones to effectors (muscles or glands) or to other neurones.

Multiple sclerosis

The disabling disease multiple sclerosis (MS) is caused by the deterioration of the myelin sheath, which slows down or inhibits the axon's ability to transmit impulses. Muscle weakness occurs and in later stages of the disease sight can be affected. The cause is as yet unknown and, despite intensive research, there is no effective treatment.

Anaesthetics work by dissolving in the myelin sheath and interfering with the transmission of nerve impulses.

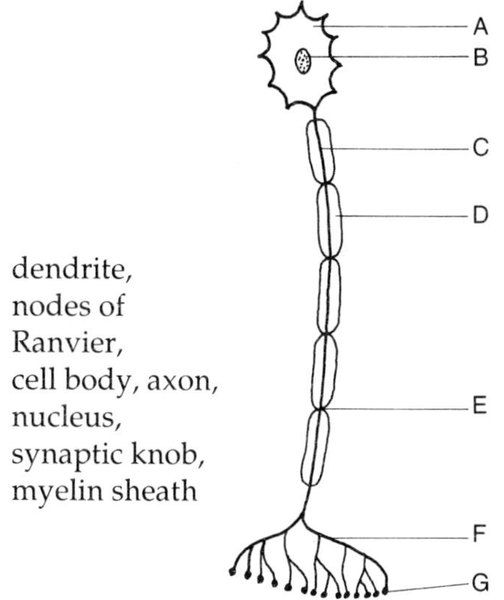

4.6 A neurone.

Synapses

At the junction between two neurones there is no physical contact. So how can an impulse 'jump' the gap (called a synapse) between the two neurones?

When an impulse reaches the synapse, a chemical is released from the end of the neurone into the gap between it and the next neurone. The chemical is called **acetylcholine (ACH)**. When the ACH reaches the next neurone on the other side of the synapse it causes this neurone to set up another electrical impulse. The membrane of this neurone releases an enzyme called **cholinesterase** which then breaks down the ACH. The effect of this is that only one impulse is able to pass at a time. Although this process happens relatively fast it does slow down the speed of the impulse a little. Therefore a reaction to a stimulus is faster if the neurone pathway contains fewer synapses.

4 Label the parts of the neurone in Fig 4.6 using the list of words next to the diagram.

Fig 4.7 shows the mechanisms involved when an impulse passes across a synapse.

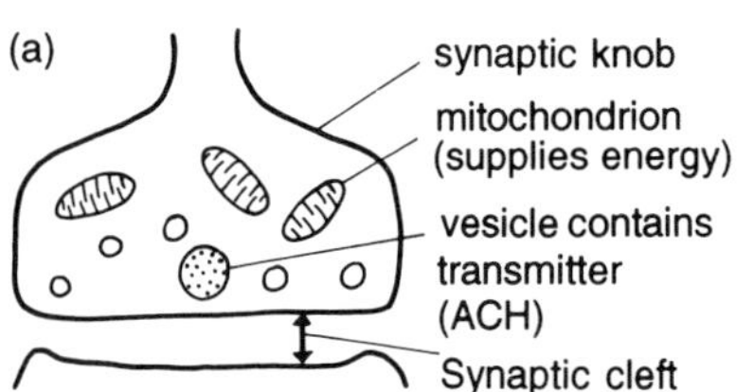

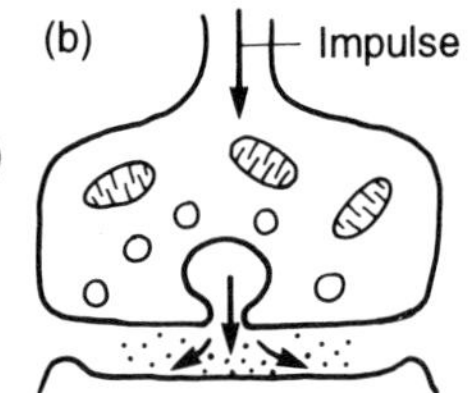

ACH released into synaptic cleft. When it reaches the other side of the synaptic cleft it depolarises the membrane of the next neurone, setting up another electrical impulse in that neurone.

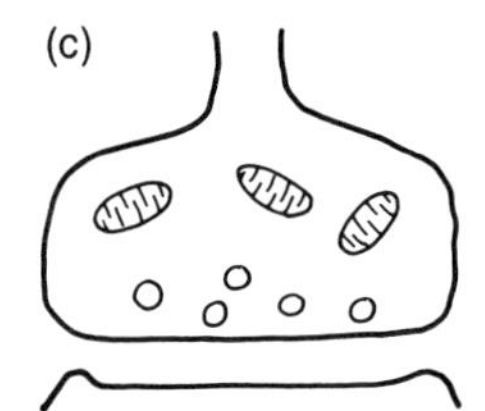

Cholinesterase on the membrane of the next neurone breaks down the ACH so that it cannot continue to 'fire' the next neurone.

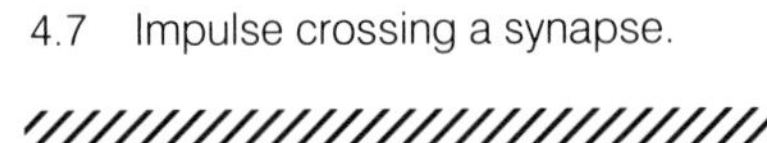

4.7 Impulse crossing a synapse.

5 The strength of an impulse must be above a certain threshold to start the release of acetylcholine into the synapse so that the message can be passed from one neurone to another. What do you think would happen if there were no such threshold to overcome?

Reflex action

There are a number of actions that we make which need no thought. These responses are sometimes called 'involuntary'. A receptor detects a stimulus and starts an impulse up a sensory neurone to the spinal cord, across a synapse and into a relay neurone. The impulse then crosses another synapse to a motor neurone. This takes the impulse to an effector which takes action against (responds to) the stimulus. The brain takes no part in this action.

6 Fig 4.8 shows a simple reflex arc. Match up the terms below it to the letters on the diagram.

7 What would be the response of this reflex arc?

8 Which term best describes this type of action? conscious/initiated/involuntary/voluntary

9 Before moving on, make sure you understand and can explain the following terms: **reflex, stimulus, receptor, effector, response**. Check them with the glossary.

10 The table below summarises some reflexes. Write down the terms missing from boxes (a) – (i).

Reflex	Stimulus	Receptor	Effector	Response
secretion	smell, sight and/or thought of food	receptor cells in nose and eyes	salivary glands	saliva is produced
blinking	bright light	retina or touch	eyelid muscle	a
knee jerk	b	stretch receptors on tendon	c	lower leg jerks upwards
movement away from pain	d	pain receptor in skin	e	foot rises off the pin
movement away from heat	picking up a hot test tube	f	g	the test tube is dropped
coughing	obstruction in the trachea	receptors in the trachea	h	i

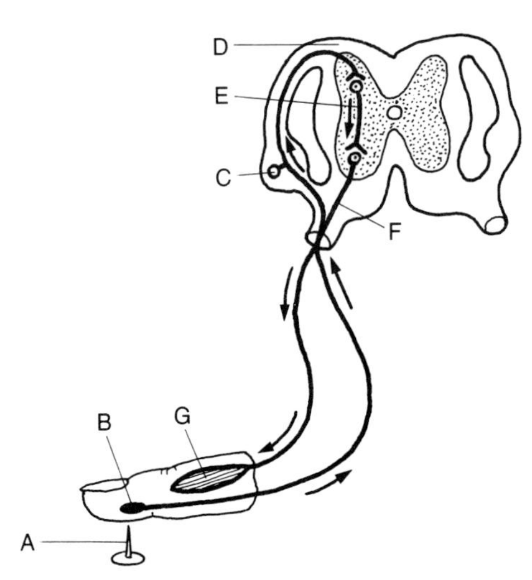

effector, motor neurone, receptor, relay neurone, sensory neurone, spinal cord, stimulus

4.8 A reflex arc.

The knee jerk reaction

Doctors often test the knee jerk reaction when they are trying to diagnose whether a patient has nerve damage caused by a bulging disc in his or her spine. As this is a reflex, the brain is not involved and so the patient cannot control this response and fake the result of the test. If the response is missing, there is almost certain to be some nerve damage.

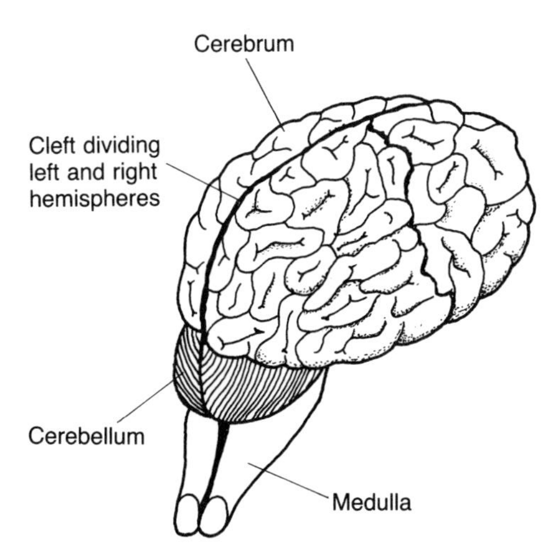

4.9 The human brain.

The human brain

There are over ten billion neurones in your brain. Your brain is more versatile than any computer that has so far been built although it is only the size of a large grapefruit. The brain is an extension of the spinal cord.

The brain has particular areas for specific functions. It consists of three main parts (Fig 4.9):

- **Cerebrum** This makes up 70 % of the total volume of the brain and is split into two halves (left and right) which are known as the **cerebral hemispheres**. This region of the brain is mainly concerned with intelligence and it also deals with the senses such as sight and hearing.
- **Medulla** This region of the brain is situated at the higher end of the spinal cord, at the base of the brain. Neurones from the spinal cord actually cross over in the medulla, which means that the left side of the brain controls the right side of the body and vice versa.
- **Cerebellum** This is a structure at the rear of the brain that is partially covered by the cerebrum. Its function is to coordinate and control our sense of balance and our movements.

Right and left brain

Each hemisphere controls different aspects of thinking. Fig 4.10 shows where these processes are 'localised'.

In most people, logical and scientific aspects are the function of the left hemisphere. Imaginative, special thinking is the responsibility of the right hemisphere.

It is usual for an individual to have one hemisphere more developed than the other. This 'dominance' of one side or the other might determine an individual's aptitude and style of thinking.

A structure called the corpus callosum (measuring about 10 cm in length), which is found in the centre of the brain, was thought of by early scientists as a link between the two hemispheres. It was therefore thought to be crucial for the brain to function correctly. This theory was thrown into doubt in the 1930s when doctors found that by surgically cutting a patient's corpus callosum in two, epileptic seizures were markedly subdued with no noticeable impairment to the patient's normal behaviour. It was a team of scientists led by Roger Sperry at the California Institute of Technology that solved the mystery and discovered the localisation of functions discussed above. They concluded that the corpus callosum unifies attention and awareness so that the right and left hemispheres of the brain share learning and memory. This won Sperry a Nobel prize in 1981.

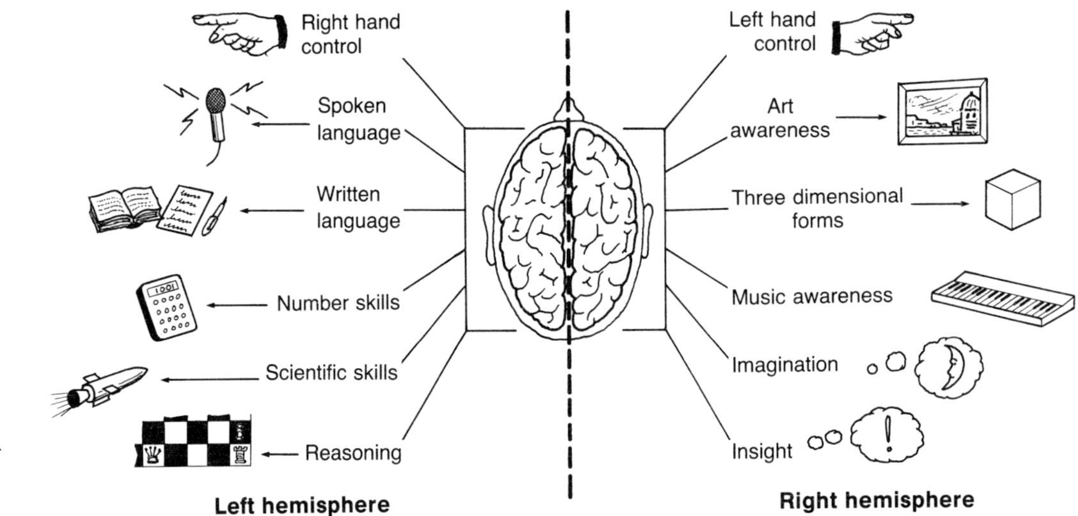

4.10 Functions of the different brain hemispheres.

Answers

1 The level of glucose in the bloodstream of a normal person would rise after eating a meal.

2

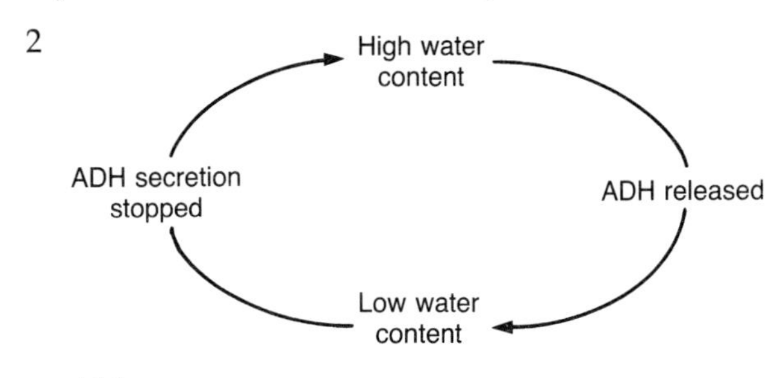

4.11

3 See glossary.

4 A cell body; B nucleus; C axon; D myelin sheath; E node of Ranvier; F dendrite; G synaptic knob

5 If the impulse is not strong enough to initiate the release of acetylcholine into the synapse then the nerve impulse will not pass from one neurone to the next and so no action or reaction will occur. If this did *not* happen, the body would respond to every tiny stimulus.

6 A stimulus; B receptor; C sensory neurone; D spinal cord; E relay neurone; F motor neurone; G effector

7 The hand would be moved away rapidly from the stimulus.

8 involuntary

9 See glossary.

10 a eyelids shut (blinking)
b tap with hammer just below knee
c thigh muscle
d stand on a pin
e muscles in leg
f heat receptors in skin
g muscles in hand and fingers
h intercostal muscles in chest and diaphragm
i obstruction removed

Chapter 5 Genetics and inheritance

Starting points

Do you understand the following terms: **sexual reproduction** and **asexual reproduction**? Write a sentence or two (no more) to explain the difference between them, then check them against the glossary at the back of the book.

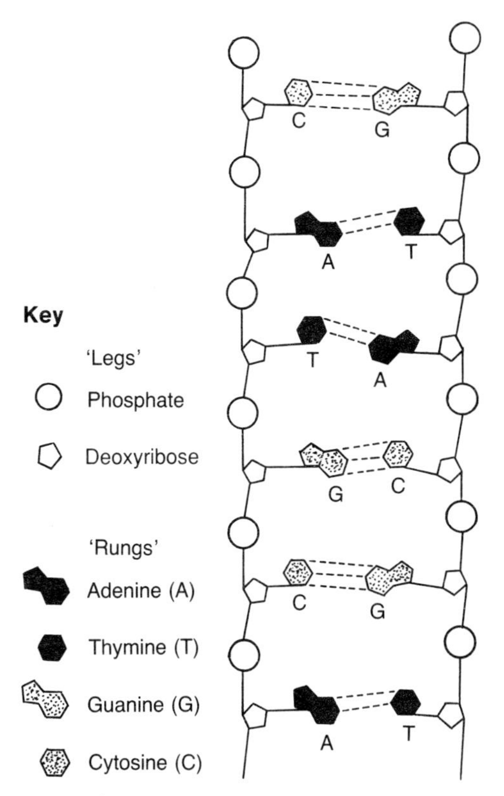

5.1 The pairing of bases in a molecule of DNA.

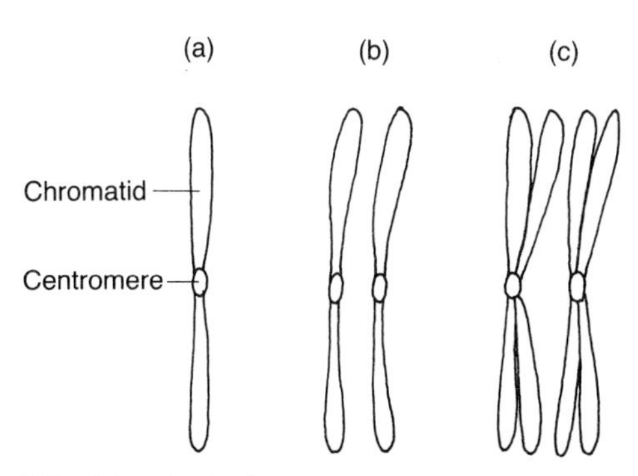

5.2 (a) a single chromosome,
(b) a homologous pair of chromosomes,
(c) a homologous pair of chromosomes that have replicated during cell division.

We all take it for granted that the offspring of human beings will be humans and that we resemble our parents. Genetics is the study of how this happens. It deals with

- how characteristics are inherited
- how development takes place
- how species evolve.

We will look briefly at all of the above, but first we must understand the nature of genetic material – the material which carries the 'instructions' for the inheritance of characteristics.

The nature of genetic material

In the **nucleus** of every cell is a number of chromosomes. Chromosomes are made of protein and a substance called **DNA (deoxyribonucleic acid)**. A strand of DNA looks very much like a ladder, with each rung in the ladder consisting of two types of molecules.These molecules are called organic **bases** and there are four types of these bases: adenine (A), thymine (T), cytosine (C) and guanine (G). These bases are rather like jigsaw pieces (see Fig 5.1). When forming the rungs of the ladder, A will only pair with T, and C will only pair with G. The legs of the ladder are made of two other types of molecules: a sugar (deoxyribose) and phosphoric acid.

Inside the nucleus

This chapter will be concerned mainly with the material found in the nucleus of cells – DNA (deoxyribonucleic acid). DNA is the material that carries the instructions for all the substances a cell has to make. It is found in the nucleus as threads called **chromosomes**. Each cell of an individual has exactly the same amount and type of DNA. In humans every cell has 46 chromosomes.

Different cells may use different instructions on the chromosomes to make substances. For example, every cell's DNA is capable of making the hormone insulin. However, only cells found in part of the pancreas actually use the instructions for insulin formation; in every other cell of the body these instructions are ignored.

Cells involved in reproduction, called **gametes**, contain half the amount of DNA found in ordinary (**somatic**) cells. In humans, for example, somatic cells contain 46 chromosomes while sperm and ova (eggs) contain only 23. When a sperm cell and an ovum fuse during fertilisation, the full complement of 46 chromosomes is restored.

The faithful copier

All cells have to divide at some time. Some divide so that the organism can grow, others divide when they are worn out or need repair. Skin cells, for example, are constantly being rubbed off the body and need to be replaced. When a normal body cell replaces itself, it must make an exact copy of itself, especially its DNA. Human somatic cells have 46 chromosomes and are called **diploid** ($2n$). **Mitosis** is the type of cell division which produces an exact copy of the original or parent cell.The DNA is copied faithfully, so that the new cells (daughter cells) each receive 46 chromosomes.

A second type of cell division also exists, called **meiosis**. Unlike mitosis, it results in daughter cells which have only half the number of chromosomes found in the parent cell. These cells are described as **haploid** (n). Meiosis takes place in the reproductive tissue of higher animals and plants and the haploid cells produced are called gametes (sperm or eggs). Each gamete formed by meiosis is slightly different in its genetic composition from every other gamete. This is because during meiosis, chromosomes often swap information, so that each one is unlike any other. This explains why you are totally unique – unless you happen to have an identical twin.

Summary

Mitosis results in daughter cells which are diploid and genetically identical to the parent cells (**clones**). Meiosis results in cells (gametes) which are haploid and genetically different from the parent cells. Meiosis is sometimes called **reduction division**. Fig 5.3 summarises these two types of cell division.

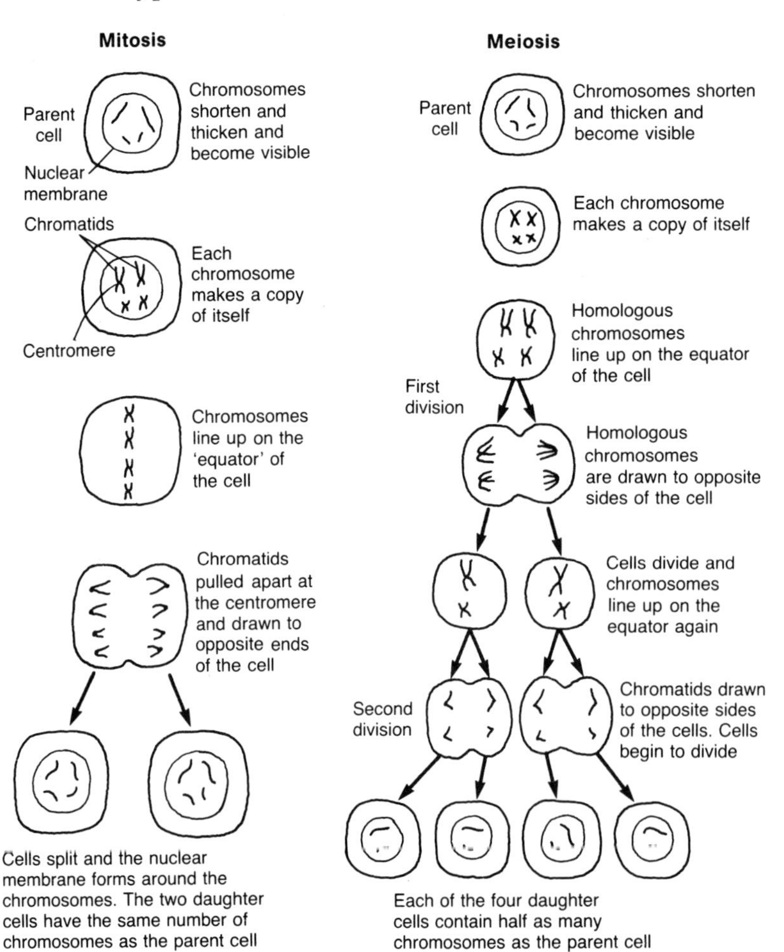

5.3 Mitosis and meiosis.

The structure and function of chromosomes

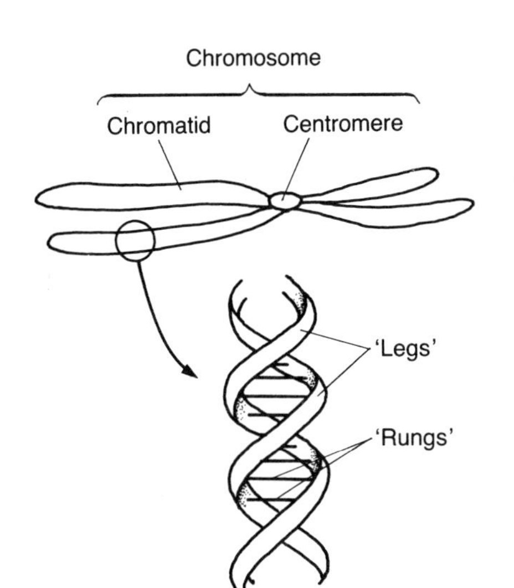

5.4 Structure of a chromosome, showing how the DNA is highly coiled.

When a cell is not dividing, it is very difficult to see the chromosomes. Then just before a cell divides, the chromosomes appear as long threads and can be seen under a microscope if they are stained.

The structure of a chromosome is shown in Fig 5.4. The chromosomes come in pairs which are like two editions of the same book – each book has the same chapters containing the same information, but presented in a slightly different way. For example, one book might contain black and white photographs while the other edition contains colour photographs.These pairs of chromosomes are called **homologous chromosomes** (homo = the same).

Each chromosome of a homologous pair carries information, or chapters, in the same place. Chapter two always follows chapter one. Each chapter is called a **gene** and its position on the chromosome is called its **locus**. Each gene is like a set of instructions, for making a particular protein. For example, chapter three (gene 3) on one chromosome of the homologous pair might give the instructions for blue eyes, while gene 3 on the other homologous chromosome might give the instructions for brown eyes. It is vital that the instructions are correct; if any of them are incorrect or missing, the results could be disastrous for the organism.

Dominant and recessive traits

The genes found at the same locus on a pair of homologous chromosomes are called **alleles**. The alleles can be the same, or they can be slightly different. An example of this is the ability to roll your tongue. There are two alleles of the gene which controls this trait. We will call them *R* and *r* (for rolling). There are three possible combinations of these alleles, *RR*, *Rr* and *rr*. It has been found that people with the combinations *RR* or *Rr* have the ability to roll the tongue, while people with the combination *rr* have not (Fig 5.5).

So any combination of *R* and *r* leads to the ability to roll the tongue, but a combination of *r* and *r* does not. When combined with *R*, the *r* allele appears to have no effect. We say that *R* is **dominant**, while *r* is **recessive**. Only when there is no dominant allele to 'mask' *r*, does the person lose the ability to roll the tongue.

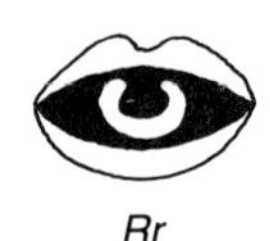

RR *Rr* *rr*

5.5 Genes for tongue rolling.

The types of genes that a person has on his or her chromosomes is called the person's **genotype**. How these genes affect us or how they make us look is called our **phenotype**.

1 Write a brief explanation of the following terms and then check them with the glossary: **gene, allele, locus, genotype, phenotype, recessive, dominant.**

Handing on to the next generation

The work of Mendel

How are our genes or characteristics handed down to our offspring? This is a question which fascinated an Austrian monk, Gregor Mendel, in the nineteenth century. His work with different varieties of pea plants led to his discovery of the existence of dominant and recessive genes, and he was able to predict accurately the phenotypes and genotypes of the offspring. He worked with 'true-breeding' pea plants, i.e. giant or dwarf plants that, when only allowed to self-pollinate, produced only giant or dwarf pea plants generation after generation.

Mendel first published his results in 1865, but very little notice was taken of his work by scientists of the day. This was partly due to the fact that his theories did not agree with those of the eminent scientist Charles Darwin. We now believe that in this case Mendel was right and Darwin was wrong.

Working with plants that have only one difference to monitor (a **monohybrid cross**), we can predict the genotype of the offspring.

Here are some worked examples, followed by some problems for you to try yourself.

If we cross two true-breeding plants which have only one genetic difference, how can we predict the offspring for two generations? Look at the following cross:

Tall plant × Dwarf plant

Because they are true-breeding, the tall plant will have the genotype *TT* and the dwarf plant *tt* (T and *t* are alleles of the gene for tallness). During the formation of gametes, ova or pollen, by meiosis (**gametogenesis**), each gamete receives one allele (Fig 5.6).

Note The term **homozygous** is used to describe an organism which has the same two alleles for a characteristic, for example *RR* or *rr* for tongue rolling. An organism which has two different alleles such as *Tt* for tallness is said to be **heterozygous**. (Homo = same, hetero = different)

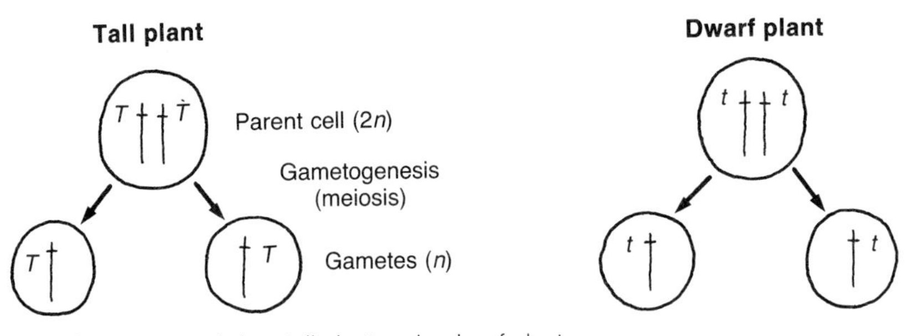

5.6 Gametogenesis in a tall plant and a dwarf plant.

During fertilisation, the gametes combine. To look at all the possible combinations, we use a Punnett square (Fig 5.7).

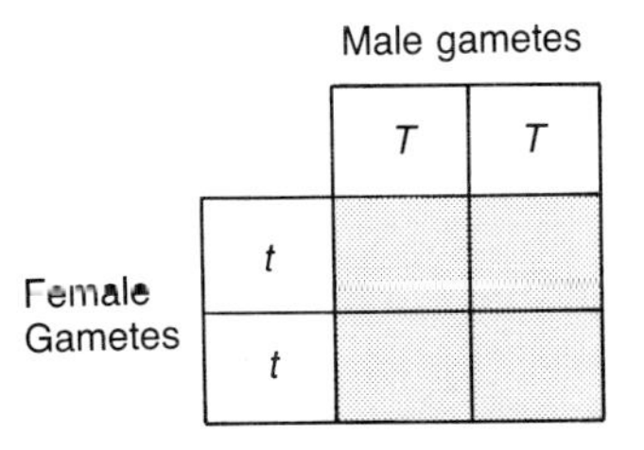

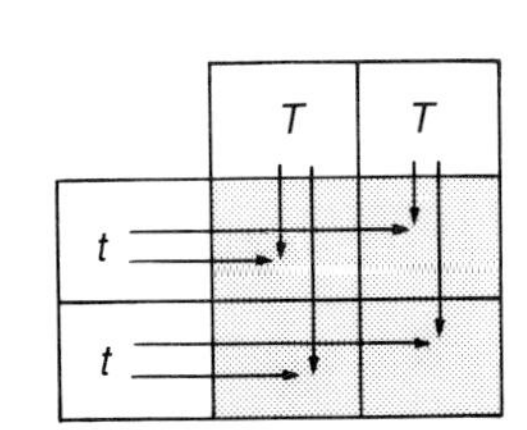

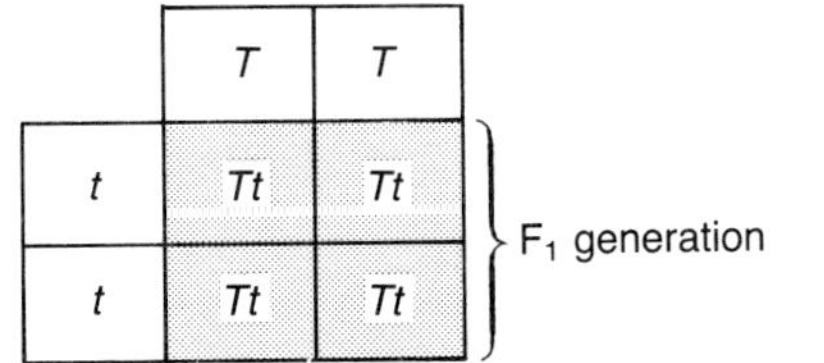

5.7 How Punnett squares are used to predict the offspring of a monohybrid cross.

In the white squares we put the male and female gametes. The shaded squares show every possible genotype in the first generation, or the F_1 **generation**. In this case they are all *Tt* – that is they are heterozygous.

A summary is given in the table opposite.

Genotype	Phenotype
100 % Heterozygous (*Tt*)	tall

To look at the offspring in the second or F_2 **generation**, we take two of the offspring from the F_1 generation and look at the gametes they produce and at all the combinations of these gametes (Fig 5.8).

Gametogenesis

Parent cell (2*n*)

Gametes (*n*)

Punnett square

	T	*t*
T	*TT*	*Tt*
t	*Tt*	*tt*

F_2 generation

5.8 Gametogenesis in the F_2 generation and a Punnett square showing the genotypes of the F_2 generation.

Using the Punnett square, the combinations in the F_2 generation are shown opposite.

Genotype	Phenotype
50 % heterozygous (*Tt*)	tall
25 % homozygous dominant (*TT*)	tall
25 % homozygous recessive (*tt*)	dwarf

This predicts that the genotypes of the second generation plants will be in the ratio 1 *TT* : 2 *Tt* : 1 *tt* and that the phenotypes will be in the ratio 3 tall : 1 dwarf.

Plants with the genotype *TT* and *Tt* will both be tall, so how can we tell the genotype of a tall plant? The best way is to perform a **back cross**, in which a plant with the dominant characteristics is crossed with a plant showing the recessive characteristics. In this case a dwarf plant is crossed with a tall one. If all the offspring are tall (*Tt*), then the tall plant must have been *TT*. If some are dwarf (*tt*), then the tall plant must have been *Tt*.

2 Draw Punnett squares for crossing a *tt* pea plant with
   a a *TT* pea plant
   b a *Tt* pea plant.
   What ratios of tall to dwarf plants would you expect in the first generation in each case?

3 a If an albino mouse has the genotype *cc* and a mouse with a normal brown coat has the genotype *CC*, work out the genotypes and phenotypic ratios of the F_1 and F_2 generations.
   b What result would indicate that the mice were true-breeding?

4 Certain varieties of tomato plants have hairy stems, while others are hairless. The gene for hairy stems (*H*) is dominant to the gene for hairless stems (*h*).
   a If a tomato plant has hairy stems, what are its two possible genotypes?
   b A hairless plant can only have one genotype. Why?
   c A hairy-stemmed plant is crossed with a hairless one and the following phenotypic ratio is obtained: 50 % hairy stems and 50 % hairless stems. Explain this result.

The dihybrid cross

Here we are dealing with organisms that differ in two characteristics. For example, round-seeded peas with a yellow cotyledon (seed leaf) and wrinkled-seeded peas with a green cotyledon.

Round seed = *R* (dominant)
Yellow cotyledon = *Y* (dominant)

Wrinkled seed = *r* (recessive)
Green cotyledon = *y* (recessive)

Fig 5.9 shows gametogenesis occurring in two parents with the genotypes *RRYY* and *rryy*.

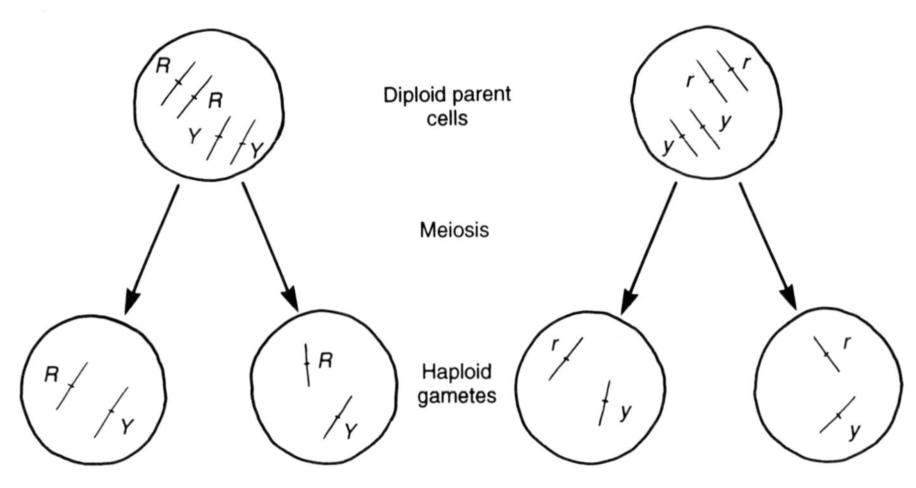

5.9 Gametogenesis in a dihybrid cross.

	RY	*RY*
ry	*RrYy*	*RrYy*
ry	*RrYy*	*RrYy*

5.10 Punnett square showing the offspring in the F_1 generation of a dihybrid cross.

Using a Punnett square, fertilisation will result in the combinations shown in Fig 5.10.

As this figure shows, all the offspring (the F_1 generation) are plants with round seeds and yellow cotyledons.

If we now look at the result of crossing these seeds (the F_2 generation), we get an interesting result.

Gametogenesis is shown in Fig 5.11(a), and the Punnett square in Fig 5.11(b) shows the result of fertilisation.

(a)

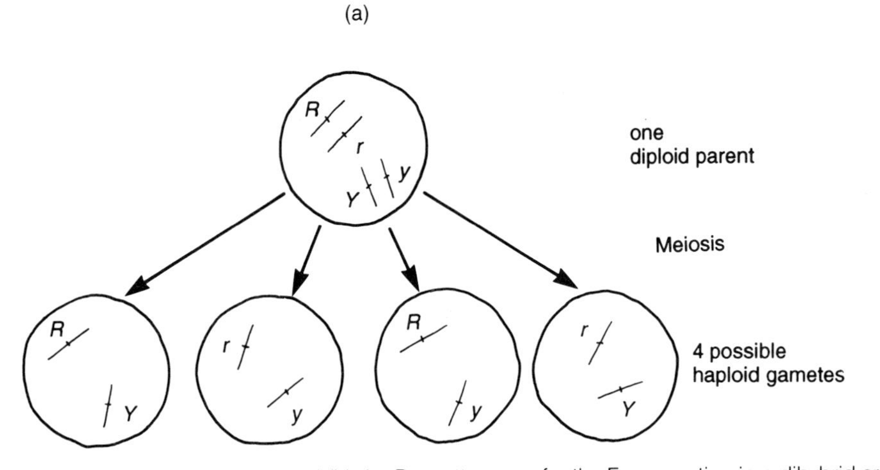

(b)

	RY	*ry*	*Ry*	*rY*
RY	*RRYY*	*RrYy*	*RRYy*	*RrYY*
ry	*rRyY*	*rryy*	*rRyy*	*rryY*
Ry	*RRyY*	*Rryy*	*RRyy*	*RryY*
rY	*rRYY*	*rrYy*	*rRYy*	*rrYY*

5.11 (a) Gametogenesis and (b) the Punnett square for the F_2 generation in a dihybrid cross.

5 Describe the characteristics of the F_2 generation shown in the Punnett square in Fig 5.11(b) and give the numbers of each different type.

Sex determination

Whether you are male or female is determined by a special pair of chromosomes called the **sex chromosomes**. These chromosomes are also known as the X and Y chromosomes. Females inherit two X chromosomes and males inherit an X chromosome and a Y chromosome. During gametogenesis (meiosis) in the ovaries, each ovum or egg receives an X chromosome. Gametogenesis in the male results in 50 % of the sperm with an X chromosome and 50 % with a Y chromosome.

The sex of a baby is determined by the type of sex chromosome contained within the sperm. If a Y sperm fertilises the egg, the baby will be a boy, if an X sperm fertilises the egg, it will be a girl (Fig 5.12).

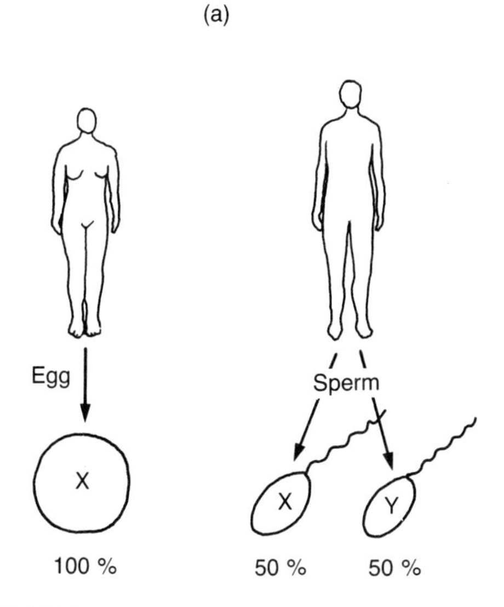

6 King Henry VIII executed two wives and divorced three others because they could not give him a son. Try to explain why no boys were born.

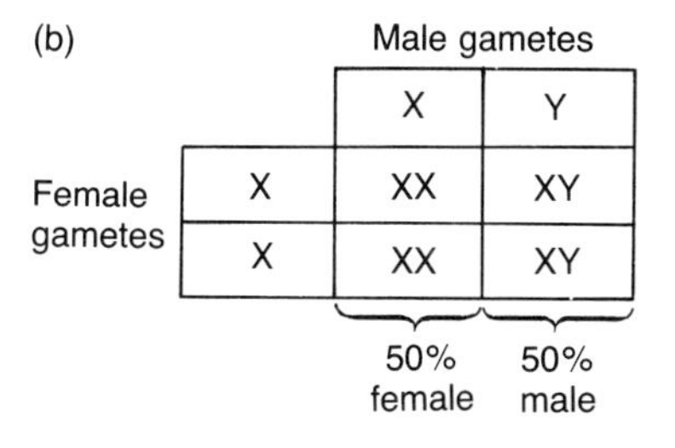

5.12 Inheritance of sex in humans. (a) Gametogenesis and (b) fertilisation.

Sex-linked inheritance

In humans, the X chromosome is larger than the Y chromosome. Genes located at the top of the X chromosome are therefore absent from the Y chromosome (Fig 5.13). This is not the case, of course, on all other homologous chromosomes, where two alleles of every gene exist.

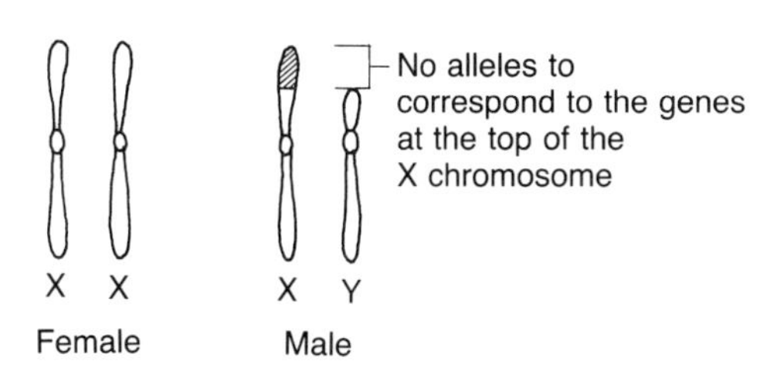

5.13 Structure of the X and Y chromosomes in humans.

The gene for the production of blood-clotting factors is known to be present on the upper part of the X chromosome. The gene for normal blood clotting (*H*) is dominant to the gene for haemophilia (*h*). A normal female will possess two dominant *H* genes. However, if a woman has one recessive gene (*h*), this will be transmitted to 50 % of her ova. If the ovum with the recessive gene is fertilised by an X-carrying sperm with a normal gene (*H*), the daughter that results will be phenotypically normal but is said to be a 'carrier' of the haemophilia gene like her mother.

7 Describe the phenotype and the genotype of the daughter.

On the other hand, if an ovum containing a recessive *h* gene on its X chromosome is fertilised by a sperm containing a Y chromosome, the son born will be a haemophiliac, having no gene on his Y chromosome to 'mask' the effects of the *h* gene.

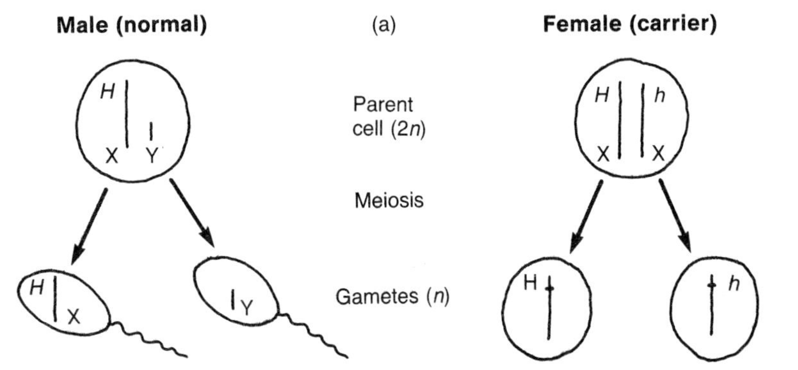

(b)

		Male gametes	
		X^H	Y
Female gametes	X^H	X^HX^H	X^HY
	X^h	X^HX^h	X^hY

5.14 Sex-linked inheritance of the blood-clotting factor gene. (a) Gametogenesis and (b) fertilisation.

Fig 5.14 shows gametogenesis in a female carrier of the haemophilia gene and in a normal male, and all the possible genotypes in the offspring of this couple.

As the Punnett square in Fig 5.14 shows, half of the female offspring are carriers and half are normal, and half of the male offspring are haemophiliacs and half are normal.

8 a When a woman carrying the recessive gene (*h*) marries a man carrying the normal gene (*H*), what are the possible genotypes of their offspring?

b The royal families of Europe have been plagued by haemophilia. Fig 5.15 shows part of the pedigree of Queen Victoria. Look at the offspring of Beatrice and Henry (whose genotypes have not been shown). Use the genotypes of the offspring to predict the genotypes of the parents.

c What could be the genotypes of the parents of a female haemophiliac?

9 In humans, normal vision is a sex-linked trait and its gene, *C*, is dominant to the allele, *c*, for red-green colour blindness. If a colour blind woman marries a man with normal vision, work out all the possible genotypes of their offspring.

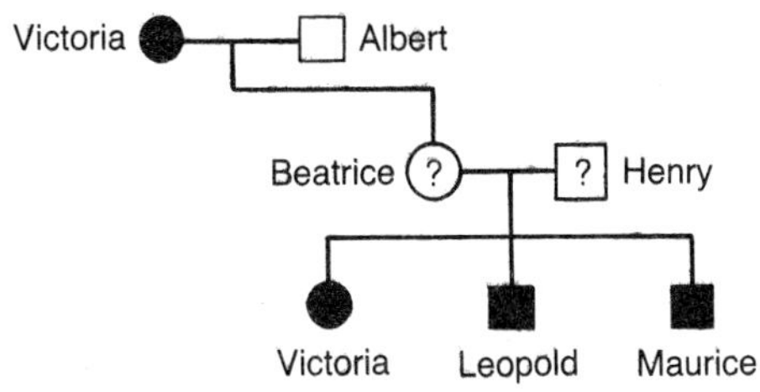

● = carrier female
□ = normal male
■ = haemophiliac male

5.15 Part of the pedigree of Queen Victoria.

Variation and selection

People are all different. They are of different heights, they have different coloured skin, different coloured eyes and different shaped ears and noses. The variation between individuals in a group can be continuous, or it can be discontinuous. An example of **continuous variation** is height. It shows a gradual transition between two extremes – very small and very tall. In a group of people you will find a few that are small, a lot of medium-sized people and a few tall people.

Sometimes there are no 'in-betweens'. For example, you can either roll your tongue or you cannot. You are either male or female, your blood will belong to one of the blood groups A, B, AB or O. This type of variation is called **discontinuous variation**.

We all vary in many ways. What we have just looked at are variations or characteristics that we inherit from our parents. Other variations may be ones which we acquire, for example, sunbathing will change the colour of fair skin.

10 Think of some examples where the environment can bring about differences between members of a species.

Variation which we inherit is brought about in the following ways:

- Genetic information is swapped between chromosomes of a homologous pair during meiosis (Fig 5.16). This results in gametes with slightly different genetic information from that of the parents.

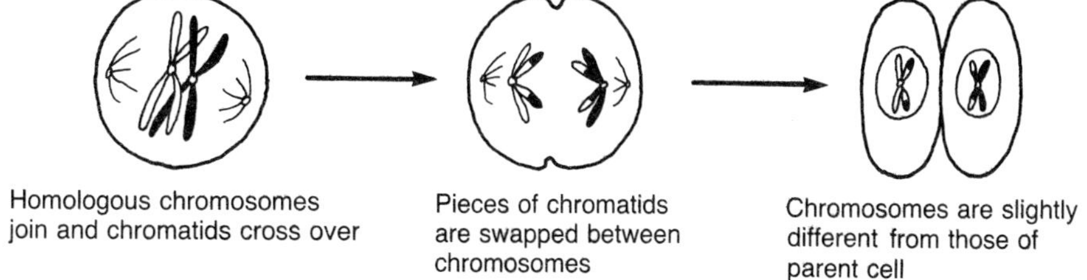

5.16 Crossing over of homologous chromosomes during meiosis.

- The pooling of genetic information from two different individuals will give rise to unique offspring.
- Genes sometimes undergo changes or **mutations**. These changes alter the type of protein they produce.

The first two types of variation mentioned above are brought about as a result of sexual reproduction. Asexual reproduction results in identical offspring.

11 a In humans, who are the only people that can be genetically identical?
   b How could the environment affect their phenotypes, that is, the way they look?

Mutations

A mutation is a spontaneous change to a chromosome or a gene that causes it to produce a different characteristic. Mutations can happen as a result of a mistake during cell division, when the DNA is not copied exactly. It can also be caused by agents called **mutagens**. Examples of these are radiation and certain chemicals like those found in cigarette smoke.

Mutations can occur in somatic (ordinary) cells or in gametes. If they happen in somatic cells, they usually go undetected. If they happen in gametes, this is usually bad news for the offspring, since the mutation will be inherited. Mutations are seldom beneficial. A mutation can be a change to a single gene, or to the number or structure of chromosomes.

Mutations that are not beneficial

Some examples of mutations with harmful consequences for the offspring are as follows:

- Down's syndrome results in an individual inheriting two chromosome number 21s (instead of one) from one parent and one chromosome number 21 from the other parent. As a result, the child has 47 chromosomes. People with this syndrome are usually mentally retarded and have characteristic facial features.
- Kleinfelter's syndrome results from inheriting an extra X chromosome in men. The affected men are sterile and often mentally retarded.
- Turner's syndrome occurs in women who inherit only one X chromosome. The affected female is sterile, does not menstruate, and is short in stature. Often, she may also have a web of skin on either side of the neck, abnormalities of the aorta and arms that angle outwards at the elbow.

About 15 % of all conceptions terminate in either a spontaneous abortion (**miscarriage**) or stillbirth. There is growing evidence that this may be a result of abnormalities in the chromosomes of the baby. In fact, over 50 % of early miscarriages have been shown to be caused by genetic abnormality. Some of these abnormalities have never been found in live-born babies and therefore are presumed to be lethal.

Selection

In a population of animals, there will be competition for food, homes and mates. When these are scarce, competition will be fierce. The healthiest, fittest, most fertile and well-adapted animals will be the most successful and are most likely to survive. The weaker members of the population are less likely to mate. The fitter ones will live longer and pass their genes on to more offspring. These stronger animals are said to have 'survival value'. This is how **natural selection** works. The pressures of the environment force the weaker members of the population to die out, and their genes go with them.

12 Think of examples of a different type of selection, **artificial selection**, where animals are deliberately bred because of their appearance, bringing about changes in the species that are not always beneficial to the animal.

Evolution of a species is brought about by natural selection. From time to time, a mutation might turn out to be beneficial, especially if there are changes in the environment or climate that are tolerated better by the mutation. Take the peppered moth for example. In 1850, the common variety was the pale speckled type. Its colouring increased its survival value, since it was very well camouflaged on lichen-covered tree trunks. By 1895, in the industrial areas of England, the black variety had risen to 98 % of the population of peppered moths. Air pollution in these areas caused the lichen to die and darkened the tree trunks. Now the dark variety had survival value.

5.17 Dark and light forms of the peppered moth on a lichen-covered tree trunk.

This type of selection occurred because of a mutation that was beneficial in the environment at that time. Mutations like this, that give rise to beneficial characteristics, allow a species to adapt to changes, even preventing its extinction. However, if the changes in the environment or climate are too rapid, this is not always possible.

13 Why do you think organisms that depend totally on asexual reproduction have difficulty in adapting to changes in the environment?

The following section on reproduction will look at the topic from a slightly different angle. We will examine some life cycles and how they may have evolved.

Reproduction

From fertilisation to death, the set of changes that takes place in an organism is called its **life cycle**. During its life cycle, an organism (animal or plant) will reproduce sexually or asexually to give rise to a new generation and the species will continue to survive. Cell division must occur in order for an organism to reproduce. In asexual reproduction, mitosis is the only type of cell division required (Fig 5.18).

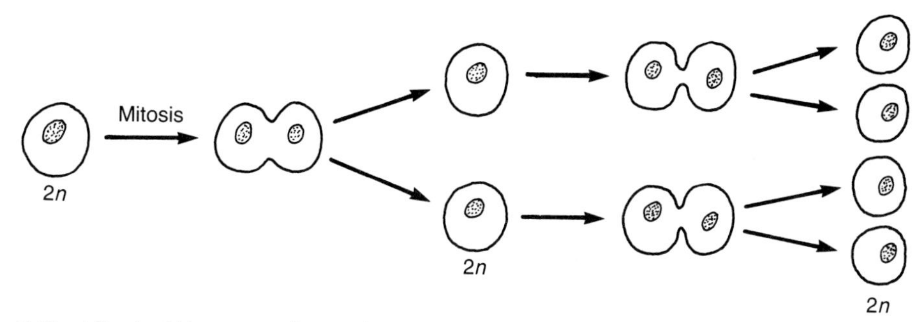

5.18 Mitosis during asexual reproduction resulting in identical offspring.

In sexual reproduction, two types of cell division are required, meiosis and mitosis.

Meiosis results in the production of haploid (n) gametes and mitosis results in the growth of the new organism following fertilisation (Fig 5.19).

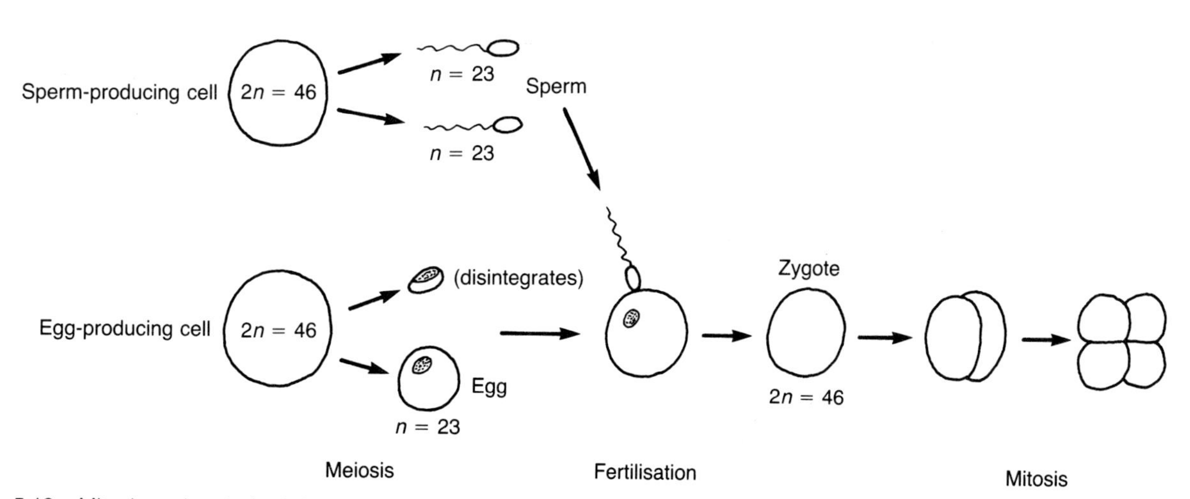

5.19 Mitosis and meiosis during sexual reproduction.

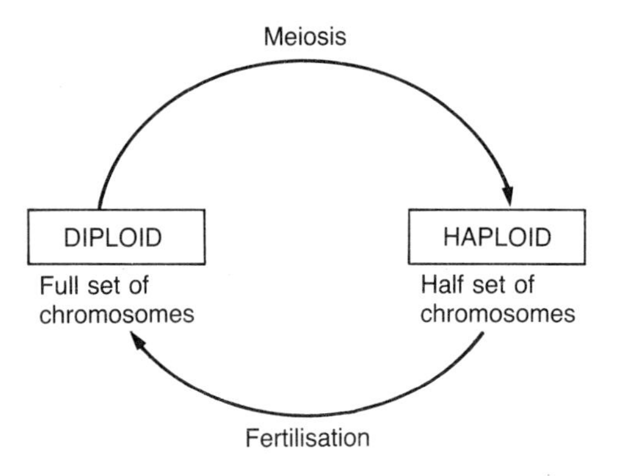

5.20 A typical life cycle.

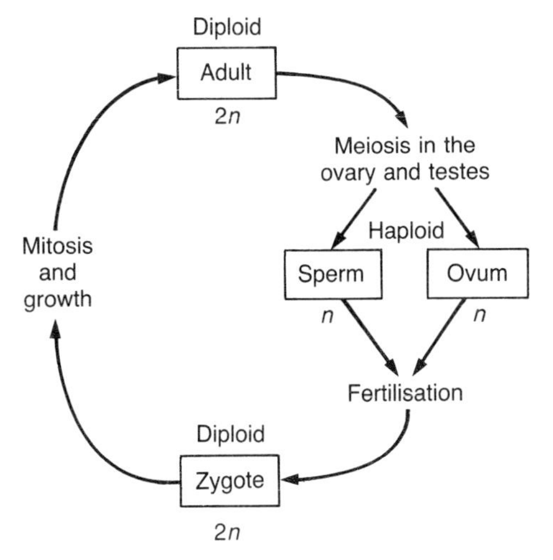

5.21 The human life cycle.

In most life cycles, there are two phases to consider, the **haploid phase** and the **diploid phase** (see Fig 5.20).

We will begin by looking at the human life cycle (Fig 5.21).

This life cycle is divided into two phases:

- meiosis to produce gametes
- fertilisation to produce a diploid cell called a **zygote**. Mitosis and growth then follow to give rise to the diploid adult.

In the life cycles of the majority of plants, there are again two stages to consider (see Fig 5.20); one which produces haploid sex cells or gametes, and one which produces a diploid plant. The way in which these stages differ from plant to plant is worth looking at. It gives us a lot of information about how the flowering plant evolved. We will look at reproduction and the life cycles in two types of plants – mosses and flowering plants.

Life cycle of mosses

The moss is known to be a very primitive plant. We will take a brief look at its life cycle.

Stage 1 The haploid plant, which is sometimes called the **gametophyte**, is the actual moss plant (Fig 5.22). All its cells have half the full number of chromosomes. Therefore, in order to produce gametes, the cells only have to divide by mitosis.

The male gametes, produced by male plants, swim through a thin film of water on the surface of the plant to the female gametes (produced by female plants). They fuse during fertilisation to produce the diploid zygote (Fig 5.23).

5.22 A sphagnum moss.

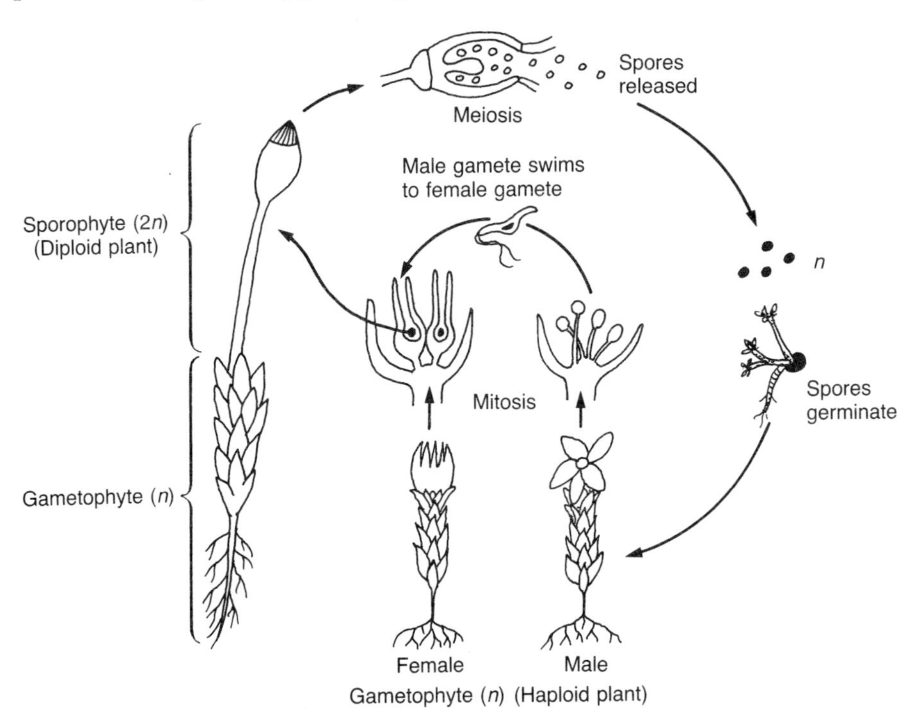

5.23 Life cycle of a moss.

Stage 2 This diploid zygote is a simple capsule on a stalk that grows out of (and is dependent on) the haploid plant. The cells of the zygote have a full set of chromosomes and it is called the **sporophyte**. The cells in the capsule undergo meiosis to produce haploid cells. These cells are called **spores**. They develop into the haploid plant which then produces the haploid gametes by mitosis – the whole process has turned a full circle.

Summary

- The gametophyte is large, long-lasting and independent of the sporophyte.
- The sporophyte is small, lasts for a relatively short period of time and is totally dependent on the gametophyte.
- Fertilisation depends on the presence of water.

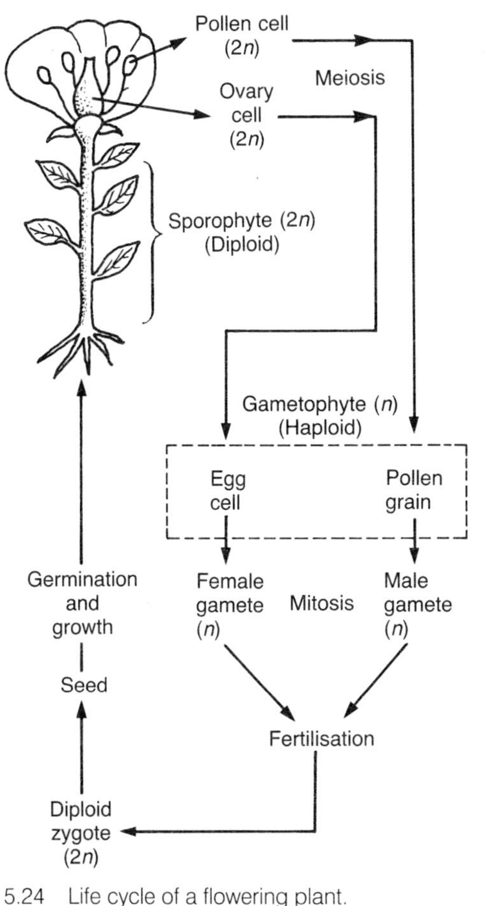

5.24 Life cycle of a flowering plant.

Life cycle of flowering plants

Moving further forward through evolutionary time, we find the flowering plants. These show a total reversal of the moss life cycle. The zygote stage, which was the short-lived stage of the moss cycle, now becomes the actual plant. The gametophyte stage, which formed the plant stage of the moss cycle, now becomes the short-lived pollen and egg cells of the flowering plant (Fig 5.24).

Fertilisation results in the formation of the diploid zygote which develops into the seed. The seed germinates and develops into the diploid plant.

Summary

- Two gametophytes are produced, one male – the pollen grain – and one female – the egg cell. They are both tiny structures which are completely incorporated into and dependent on the sporophyte plant.
- Pollination and fertilisation are achieved by making use of wind and insects.
- Fertilisation is not dependent on the presence of water.

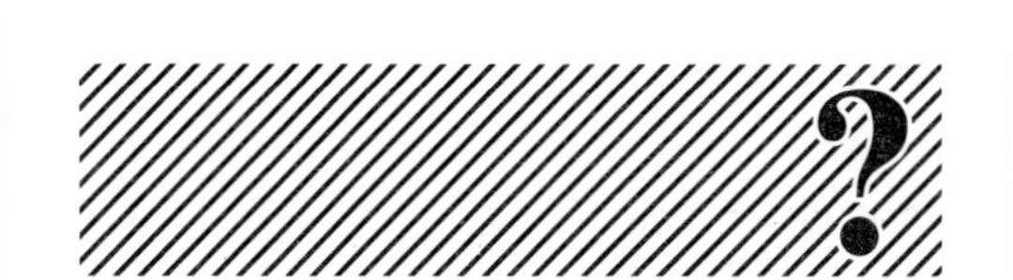

14 In terms of chromosome numbers, what is the difference between the cells of the gametophyte and the sporophyte?

15 a Draw a table for mosses and flowering plants to show, in each case, the duration and size of
(i) the gametophyte
(ii) the sporophyte.

b What is the significance of the different durations of each plant stage above?

16 a Compare the methods of fertilisation of mosses and flowering plants.

b In the case of flowering plants, how have its methods of fertilisation led to it being better adapted to the environment than the mosses?

Answers

1 See glossary.

2 (a) $TT \times tt$

	T	T
t	Tt	Tt
t	Tt	Tt

F_1 generation = 4 tall : 0 dwarf

(b) $Tt \times tt$

	T	t
t	Tt	tt
t	Tt	tt

F_1 generation = 1 tall : 1 dwarf

5.25 Punnett squares.

3 a F_1 generation : genotypes, all *Cc*; phenotypes, all brown.
F_2 generation : genotypes, *Cc* : *CC* : *cc* = 2 : 1 : 1; phenotypes, brown : albino = 3 : 1.

b If the mice were true-breeding (*CC*), all the offspring would be brown (*Cc*).

4 a *HH* and *Hh*.

b The *h* gene is recessive. If it were heterozygous (*Hh*), the *h* gene would be masked by the dominant *H* gene. The only possible genotype, therefore, is *hh*.

c The genotype of the hairy-stemmed parent must have been *Hh*. *Hh* × *hh* gives the following combinations: *Hh*, *Hh*, *hh* and *hh*.

5 Nine round with yellow cotyledons; three round with green cotyledons; three wrinkled with yellow cotyledons; one wrinkled with a green cotyledon.

6 The man is responsible for passing the Y chromosome on to his offspring. Which sperm (a Y sperm or an X sperm) fertilises the egg will determine the sex of the baby. The chance of passing on a Y is therefore 50 : 50, but unfortunately Henry passsed on an X chromosome each time!

7 Genotype = *Hh*. Phenotype = normal, i.e. she appears to be normal but she is in fact a carrier.

8 a *HH* (female, normal); *Hh* (female, carrier); *H*– (male, normal; *h*– (male, haemophiliac).

b Beatrice : *Hh*, carrier; Henry: *H*–, normal.

c Mother: *hh* or *Hh*; father: *h*–.

9 *C* = normal vision, *c* = red-green colour blindness. Genotype of woman = *cc*, man = *C*–. Genotypes of offspring = *Cc* (female, carrier), *c*– (male, colour blind).

10 Examples could include grass species that show a range of tolerance to normally poisonous metals in soil such as lead and copper – they have adapted to growing around open-cast mines where no other plants will grow. Also poor diet can result in smaller individuals.

11 a Identical twins.

b Twins that have been brought up apart may have very different personalities, depending on their upbringing. If one twin has a poor diet, he or she will probably be smaller.

12 Examples include pedigree dogs such as British bulldogs, which have been artificially selected and bred for their appearance. This has changed a lot, the very short, thick neck and broad chest being preferred by breeders. As a result, this breed often experiences breathing difficulties.

13 Asexual reproduction results in identical offspring, or clones. The ability to adapt to environmental change is dependent on new genetic combinations. The only way these occur in asexual organisms is by mutation.

14 Cells of gametophytes contain half the number of chromosomes and cells of sporophytes contain the full number of chromosomes.

15 a

		Mosses	**Flowering plants**
Gametophyte	**Duration**	long-lasting	short-lived
	Size	large	small
Sporophyte	**Duration**	short-lived	long-lived
	Size	small	large

b It shows an evolutionary change. Mosses have a very conspicuous gametophyte, which depends totally on water for fertilisation. In flowering plants, the gametophyte is incorporated into the sporophyte; the two stages have evolved to co-exist.

16 a Mosses require the presence of a thin film of water on the surface of the plant in order for the male gametes to swim to the female gametes. In flowering plants, the male gametes no longer need to be mobile since the plant makes use of carrying agents such as wind and insects. The flowering plant does not have to depend on water.

b Flowering plants are adapted to living on dry land. Also, using wind and insects to carry the gametes means they are spread further. This increases the genetic variability of the offspring, and gives a better chance of fertilisation since they do not have to rely only on the gametes from nearby plants. Because the gametes do not have to be mobile, flowering plants are able to make greater numbers of male gametes since they take less energy to make. This is another way of making sure that the plant's genes survive.

Chapter 6 Microbes

Starting points

1 You should be able to draw and label a diagram of (a) a simple plant cell and (b) a simple animal cell. Check with the answer section before continuing.

Introduction

Microbiology is the study of **microorganisms**. These are the members of a large group of free-living cells that can exist singly or as clusters. This is one of the basic differences between cells of microbes and those of animals and plants, which can exist only as part of a larger **multicellular** organism. A single microbial cell is able to carry out all the processes necessary for life – nutrition, respiration, excretion, reproduction and growth – independent of other cells.

Cell structures

All organisms fall into two categories, **prokaryotes** and **eukaryotes**, as shown in the table opposite.

Types of organisms

Prokaryotes	**Eukaryotes**
blue-green algae bacteria	fungi algae plants animals

The important difference between the two groups is in the structure of the cell nucleus. Prokaryotes have a single strand of DNA free in the **cytoplasm**, whereas in eukaryotes the DNA is enclosed in a membrane, forming a true nucleus. This suggests that eukaryotes evolved from prokaryotes.

Prokaryotes have another difference – they possess a **cell wall** (different from that of a plant cell) which gives the organism its rigidity and shape.

Bacteria

Bacterial cells are extremely small, ranging in length from 1 μm to 20 μm (1 μm = 0.001 mm). They are generally classified according to their shape. Fig 6.1 shows the shapes of different types of bacteria.

Sphere (coccus)	
pair	e.g. *Diplococcus*; causes pneumonia
chain	e.g. *Streptococcus*; causes sore throats
clump	e.g. *Staphylococcus*; causes boils
Rod (bacillus)	e.g. *Escherichia coli*; harmless bacterium found in the human intestine, and *Clostridium*; causes tetanus
Bent rod (vibrio)	e.g. *Vibrio cholerae*; causes cholera
Spiral (spirillium)	e.g. *Treponema*; causes syphilis

6.1 Classification of bacteria according to shape.

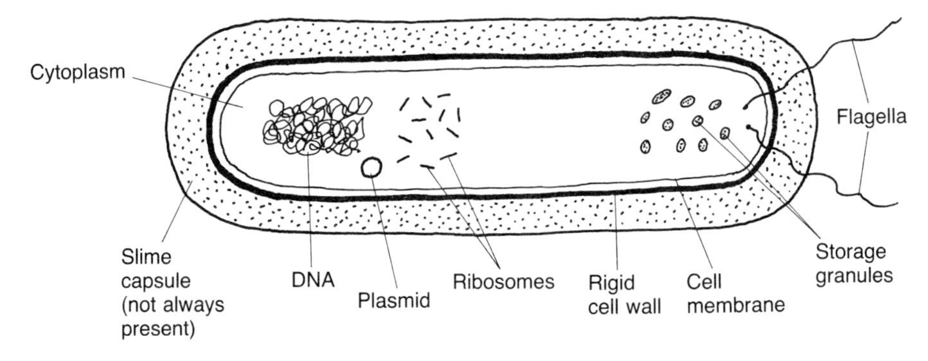

6.2 General structure of a bacterium.

Figure 6.2 shows the structures within a generalised bacterial cell. We will see how some of these structures give bacteria survival value.

The cell wall

The bacterial cell wall is made up of a complex mixture of proteins, sugars and lipids (fats). This is unlike the plant cell wall, which is made up of cellulose. Some bacteria have a **slime capsule** outside their cell wall.

There are two types of cell walls to be found in bacteria so we can divide them into two distinct groups – **Gram-positive** bacteria, G^+, and **Gram-negative**, G^-. These names derive from the staining technique, Gram's method, (used to view bacteria more easily under the microscope) which gives different results according to the type of cell wall they possess. Fig 6.3 shows the different structures of the G^+ and G^- cell walls. G^+ bacteria have a thick, single-layered wall, while G^- bacteria have two thin walls.

Cell wall
Membrane
Gram-positive

Cell wall
Membrane
Gram-negative

6.3 Cell walls of Gram-positive and Gram-negative bacteria.

The cell membrane

Sometimes called the plasma membrane, this is a thin structure that completely surrounds the cell. This vital structure is a critical barrier separating the inside of the cell from its environment. If the membrane is broken, the cell will die.

2 If you had to design an agent which would kill bacteria (a **bactericide**), how would you make use of the last piece of information given above?

Inside the cell

The DNA in bacterial cells is a highly folded, single chromosome which forms a loop or circle. In many bacteria, a separate circle of DNA has also been discovered. This is called a **plasmid**. A plasmid is completely independent of the chromosome. It can make copies of itself and, most importantly, it can transfer copies of itself to other bacteria. We will see why this is important later.

Also found in the cytoplasm are **storage granules**, containing glycogen, lipids and other food reserves, and **ribosomes**, which are responsible for protein synthesis.

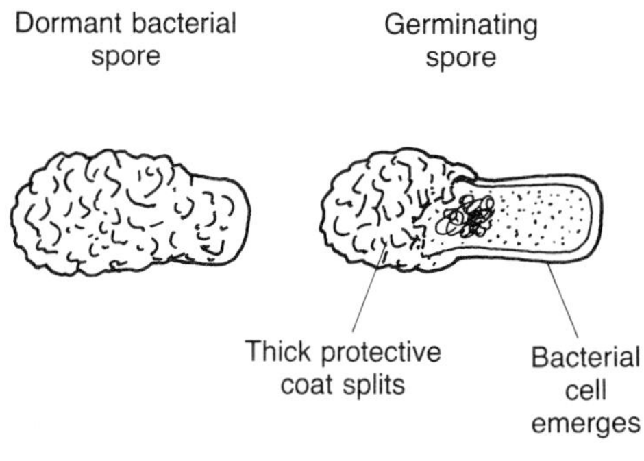

6.4 Bacterial spore.

Some bacteria possess tail-like structures called **flagella**. These bring about movement by a whip-like action, propelling the cell along.

How bacteria survive harsh conditions

A characteristic of certain rod-shaped bacteria is that under certain conditions, usually when food supplies are exhausted or they are running short of water, they are able to form a resting cell called an **endospore**. This allows the bacterium to survive very high temperatures and changes in pH. The thick protective coat of the spore allows the cell to remain dormant for a very long time. When suitable conditions return, the spore germinates to produce a single bacterial cell (see Fig 6.4). This has very serious implications for food storage and preservation.

Spores

Spores that have been dormant for thousands of years have been found in the tombs of the Egyptian mummies! This has given scientists an important insight into the types of diseases that the ancient Egyptians suffered from.

The astronauts who landed on the Moon were isolated in sealed living quarters for some days after their return to ensure that they had not brought back any 'Moon spores'.

3 What sort of precautions would you take against spores when storing, preserving or preparing food?

Reproduction

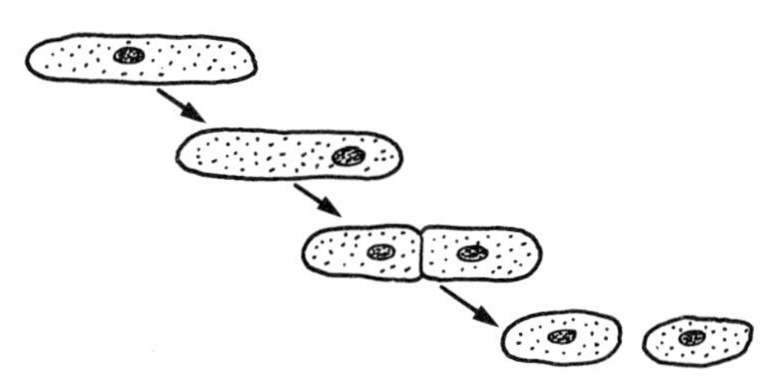
6.5 Binary fission in bacteria.

Bacteria reproduce mainly asexually, by a method known as **binary fission** (see Fig 6.5). The cell grows until it reaches its maximum size, the DNA replicates itself and the cell divides to give two identical daughter cells. This process takes about 20 minutes. It has been estimated that if division continued at this rate, after 26 hours a single bacterium (0.001 mm in length) would have produced enough offspring to occupy a volume of 1000 m^3 (about the size of a house)!

This, of course, would not happen in practice, since many bacteria would die before they reproduced, nutrients would run out, or they would be poisoned by their own toxic waste.

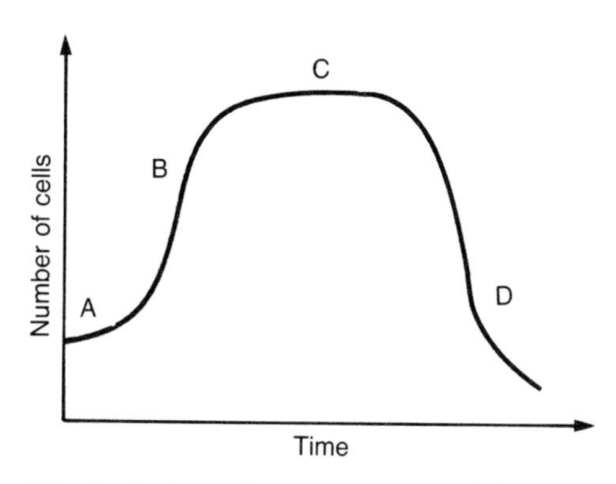

6.6 Typical growth curve for a bacterial population.

Fig 6.6 shows a typical growth curve for a population of bacteria grown on nutrient agar.

The graph is divided into four phases as follows:

A **The lag phase.** The bacteria are 'settling in', becoming adjusted to their new environment.

B **The logarithmic phase.** The bacteria begin to divide and multiply. This phase is also known as the phase of **exponential growth** – each cell in the population is dividing to form two cells.

C **The stationary phase.** This shows no increase or decrease in the numbers. This may be due to competition between bacteria for food, space or oxygen. A build-up of wastes may cause undesirable changes in the environment.

D **The death phase.** The bacteria begin to die because of the lack of oxygen and food and because of the build-up of toxic waste.

Nutrition

Like all organisms, bacteria require a constant supply of nutrients in order to obtain energy and the raw materials needed to build their cells. They do this in a wide variety of ways (see box).

Nutrition in bacteria

Autotrophic bacteria. These are capable of synthesising their food from inorganic materials. They can be subdivided into the **photosynthetic** autotrophs and the **chemosynthetic** autotrophs.

- Photosynthetic autotrophs use sunlight as a source of energy, for example, the blue-green algae.
- Chemosynthetic autotrophs get their energy from chemical reactions, for example the nitrifying bacteria in the nitrogen cycle.

Heterotrophic bacteria. These cannot synthesise their own food and require a supply of organic material. They can be subdivided into **saprophytes** and **parasites**.

- Saprophytes use non-living sources of organic material, for example the bacteria of decay.
- Parasites use a living source of organic material, for example disease-causing bacteria.

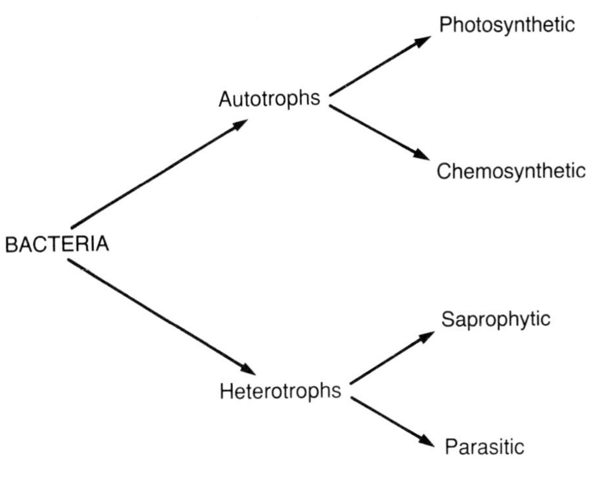

6.7 Nutrition in bacteria.

Bacterial respiration

Bacteria can respire aerobically or anaerobically. Most bacteria are aerobic. Anaerobic bacteria may produce lactic acid, acetic acid or ethanol as a by-product. Some bacteria can only respire in the absence of oxygen. Others can respire with or without oxygen.

Bacteria and humans

Some bacteria can be very harmful to us while others play an essential role in our lives.

An example of bacteria that are harmful to us is those which take nitrogen from the soil and reduce its fertility.

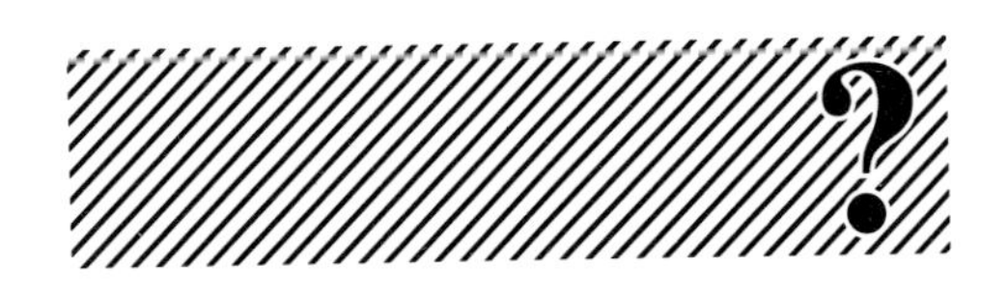

4 Give some other examples of bacteria which are harmful to humans.

Pathogens

Pathogens are parasites. A parasite is an organism that lives on and causes damage to another living organism, called the **host**. The two form a host–parasite relationship and the outcome of this relationship depends on two factors:

- How pathogenic (or **virulent**) the parasite is, in other words, how much damage it can inflict on the host.
- How susceptible or resistant the host is to the parasite.

When pathogens enter the body, we become infected. This does not mean that we have a disease, but if the parasite is not checked and destroyed, its numbers may rise to a level which causes disease.

Pathogenic organisms can gain entry to the body through the skin (via a wound), or through mucus membranes in the lungs or the intestines (from our food).

Once inside the body, in order to do any damage the pathogen must multiply. Pathogens bring about damage to the host in many ways. Most produce **toxins** (poisonous chemicals) which are responsible for most or all of the damage. When released, these toxins can spread around the body, damaging tissue far away from the site of the infection.

Here are some examples of diseases caused by toxin-producing bacteria.

Diphtheria. This disease is transmitted by droplet infection, that is, when someone already infected coughs or sneezes, the droplets of saliva sprayed from the mouth carry the bacteria. The toxin produced causes the lining of the air passages to become inflamed. It destroys heart muscle and other tissues.

Tetanus. Sometimes called lockjaw, this disease develops as the result of a deep cut from a dirty object, such as a nail. The toxin attacks the nervous system and causes muscle paralysis.

Botulism. The bacterium itself rarely grows inside the body, but does grow and produce the toxin in improperly canned food. Eating the food results in paralysis and is often followed by death. This toxin is one of the most poisonous substances known. One milligram of the pure toxin is enough to kill more than one million guinea pigs. Death is usually due to respiratory or cardiac failure.

Human defences against disease

The human body is constantly under attack from pathogens. In order to stay healthy, the body must have a way of dealing with them. Our first line of defence is our **natural immunity**.

5 Describe how our bodies prevent the entry of bacteria into our systems.

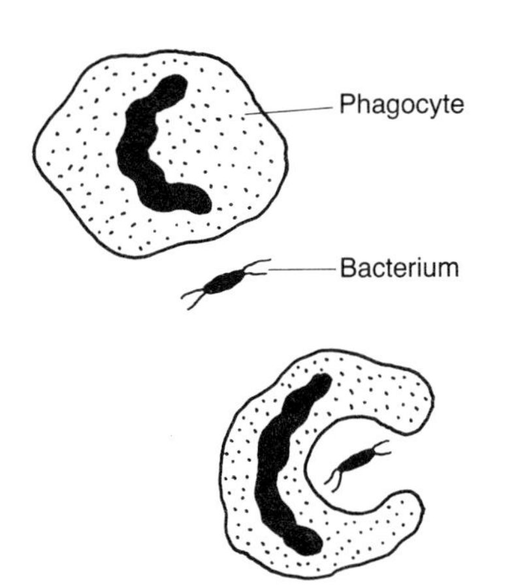

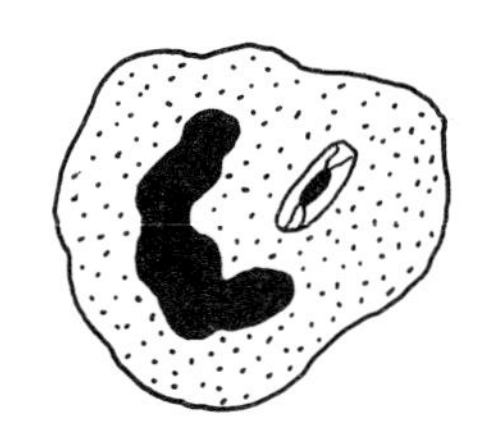

6.8 The action of a phagocyte as it surrounds, engulfs and destroys a bacterium.

If bacteria do enter, the system is backed up by:

- blood clotting, to prevent the entry of more bacteria
- **phagocytes**, white blood cells, which engulf and destroy bacteria (see Fig 6.8). In the process, the phagocytes themselves die, forming the yellow pus found in an infected cut.

Acquired immunity

This is our second line of defence. It is called 'acquired immunity' because we are not born with it: it is something we build up over a long period of time.

Bacterial cells have on their surfaces chemical substances called **antigens**. When we become infected with a pathogen for the first time, other white blood cells, the **leucocytes**, learn to recognise the antigens. They produce **antibodies** in response to them. The antibodies then attach themselves to the bacteria. This either causes the bacteria to clump together, making it easier for the phagocytes to engulf them, or neutralises the bacterial toxin.

Antibodies are specific, that is, a leucocyte will produce an antibody that will attack only one type of bacterial cell (see Fig 6.9).

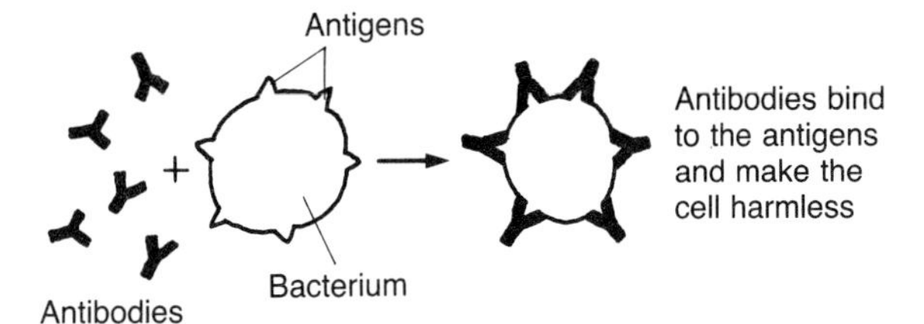

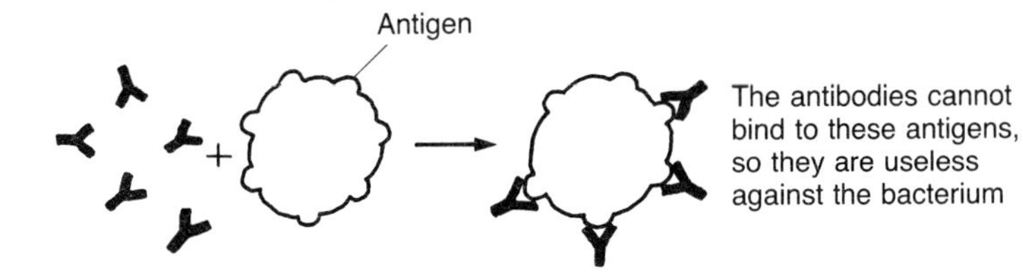

6.9 Production of antibodies in response to a specific type of antigen.

Once the body has been infected, leucocytes learn to recognise the particular bacterium and are prepared to produce antibodies rapidly the next time it invades.

6 AIDS stands for **A**cquired **I**mmune **D**eficiency **S**yndrome. AIDS victims do not die from AIDS, but from common infections such as a cold, influenza or pneumonia. Can you explain why this is so?

Antibiotics

Antibiotics are chemicals produced by microorganisms that kill or prevent the growth of other microorganisms, without damaging the host.

7 Some antibiotics can be taken orally (by mouth). What important characteristic must they have in order to be taken in this way?

Antibiotics

Here are some examples of common antibiotics:

Penicillin: discovered by Alexander Fleming in 1928. It is produced by the fungus *Penicillium notatum*. Penicillin works by preventing the synthesis of the cell wall when the bacteria are dividing. This leaves the cell vulnerable to attack by phagocytes. Penicillin is effective against a large number of pathogens.

Fleming discovered penicillin following the accidental contamination of a bacterial culture by a mould – usually an indication of sloppy technique! The mould killed the growing bacteria. Surprisingly, Fleming did not follow up his observation and it was some years later that a team including Howard Florey, Ernst Chain and N G Heatley extracted enough penicillin to try it out on patients. The results were spectacular. During World War II, penicillin saved the lives of thousands of soldiers who would otherwise have died from infected wounds.

Tetracycline: This is effective against a wide range of bacteria. For this reason, it is called a **broad spectrum antibiotic**.

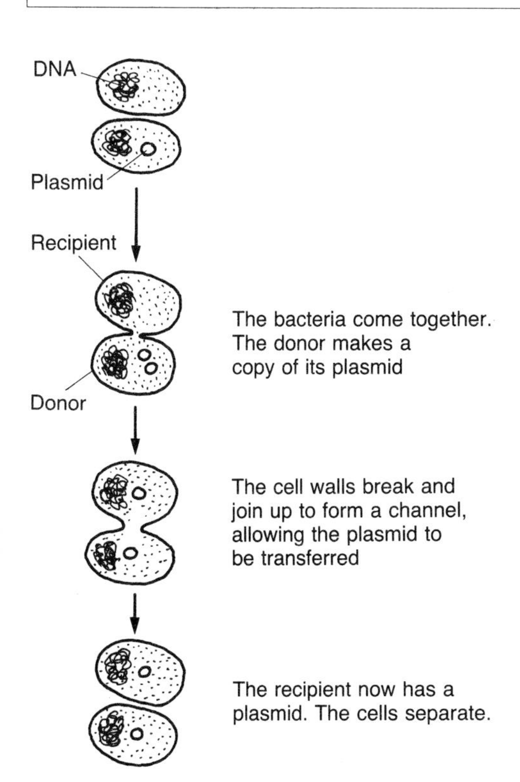

6.10 Transfer of plasmids between bacteria.

Antibiotic resistance

Penicillin is not nearly as effective against pathogens as it used to be. More and more bacteria have become resistant to it, as is the case with many of our popular antibiotics. This is because for many years antibiotics were over-prescribed by doctors – not their fault, since no-one knew at the time that bacteria have a very clever way of becoming resistant to antibiotics.

We know now that a bacterium that is resistant to an antibiotic can pass this resistance on. This is how the immunity spreads. Many bacterial cells contain little rings of DNA called plasmids and these often have genes that code for antibiotic resistance. Plasmids can pass copies of themselves on to neighbouring bacterial cells (see Fig 6.10). It is for this reason that, in the war against pathogens, they are always a few steps ahead of us.

Useful bacteria

Often when we think about bacteria, we remember only the ones that are harmful to us. The majority of bacteria are harmless and indeed many are essential to us, playing a vital part in both the nitrogen and the carbon cycles.

?

8 Give a brief account of the role of bacteria in
 a the nitrogen cycle b the carbon cycle.

Biotechnology

Biotechnology could be compared to factory farming, using microorganisms instead of chickens. It means applying biology to the manufacturing industry. Although the term itself is relatively new, many of the processes have been with us for centuries. For example, fermentation: anaerobic respiration in yeast cells yielding ethanol. This technique has been in use since before 6000 BC.

9 Make a list of any processes which you think involve biotechnology.

Food from bacteria

Pruteen – a high protein food – is simply made from dried, squashed bacterial cells. It is used as animal food. Bacteria are placed in a gigantic fermenter. They are supplied with a simple organic food, which in this case is methanol, a suitable temperature and some essential mineral salts. The fermenter is kept sterile – no other microorganisms must be allowed to contaminate it. The bacteria grow and multiply in the fermenter thus converting the methanol into bacterial protein.

Single-cell protein (SCP) is a high protein food made from a fungus such as yeast. It is fermented, with sugar as a food, in a similar way to pruteen (see Fig 6.11). This high protein food could be a cheap and effective way of solving the world food shortage, without having to breed more animals for meat.

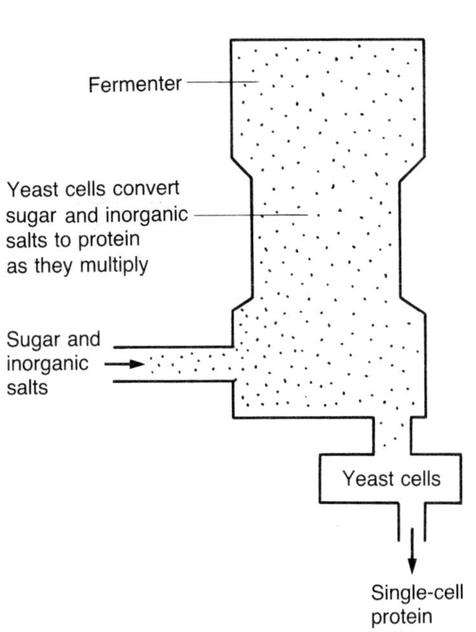

6.11 A fermenter used to make SCP.

Genetic engineering

Genetic engineering makes use of the fact that bacteria can be 'persuaded' to make a product they would not normally produce. By transferring human genes into bacterial chromosomes and allowing the bacteria to multiply, they will make the product which the human genes give instructions for.

Human growth hormone is a good example. If a child does not produce enough of this, he or she will not grow. It can be cured by giving the child injections of human growth hormone. This used to be difficult and expensive to obtain. However, by genetically engineering bacteria to make growth hormone, large amounts of it can now be produced. Fig 6.12 shows how bacteria are 'engineered' (fitted with an appropriate section of human DNA).

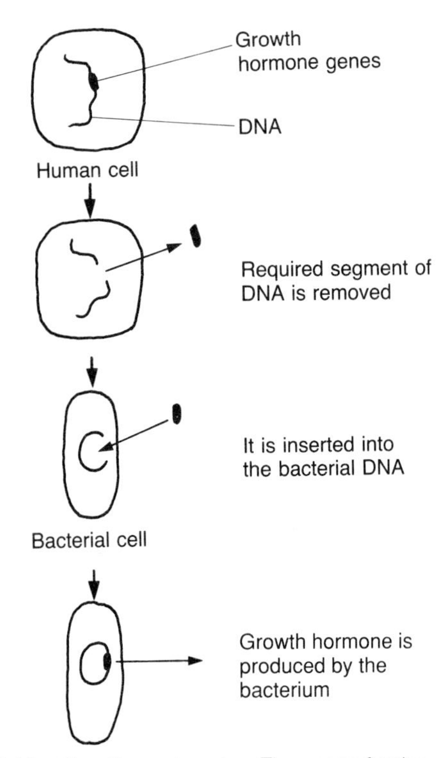

6.12 Genetic engineering. The genes for the synthesis of human growth hormone are inserted into bacterial DNA. The bacterium then produces the hormone.

Monoclonal antibodies

A similar technique has been developed to produce so-called **monoclonal antibodies**. When large numbers of identical cells are produced, they are called clones. When large numbers of one *type* of cell are produced, they are called monoclonal cells. For example, when the blood is invaded by microbes, this stimulates the rapid synthesis of lymphocytes. Only one type of lymphocyte will multiply, since the antibodies they produce are specific for one strain of bacteria. They in turn produce many identical antibodies, which attach themselves to the bacteria (Fig 6.13).

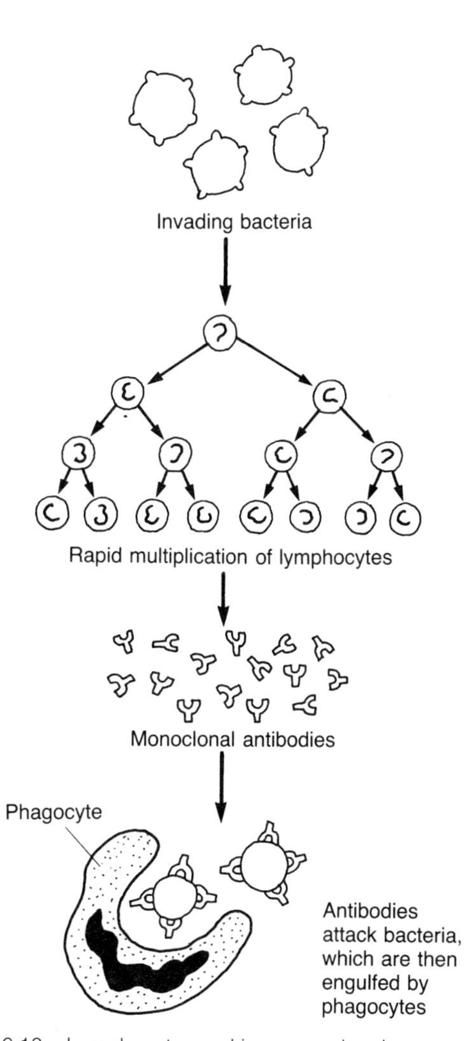

6.13 Lymphocytes making monoclonal antibodies in response to an infection.

It is now possible to make monoclonal antibodies in the laboratory, using special cells. Lymphocytes will not live and divide outside the body. However it was discovered that by making a hybrid between a lymphocyte and a tumour cell, the hybrid cells could live outside the body and make monoclonal antibodies. Because antibodies are specific for antigens or cell surface proteins, monoclonal antibodies can now be made which 'target' specific cells. These antibodies have many exciting uses. Some examples are given below.

Targeting drugs. A monoclonal antibody could be developed which is specific for proteins on the cell surfaces of a diseased organ. A drug could be attached to the antibody, which would then carry the drug directly to the diseased organ instead of being spread around the body. Fig 6.14 shows how this could be achieved.

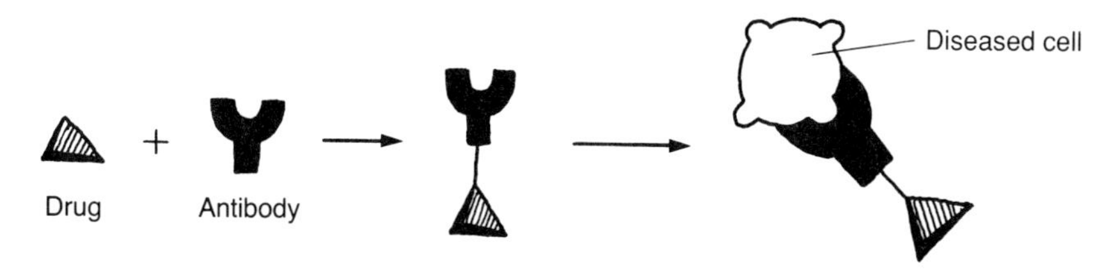

6.14 Using monoclonal antibodies for targeting drugs.

Purifying proteins. A particular protein could be extracted from a mixture of proteins by developing a monoclonal antibody specific for that protein. The antibodies would bind to that protein only, allowing it to be removed from the mixture. In this way, the monoclonal antibodies act as a sort of biological 'magnet'. They can also be used in this way to detect the presence of certain proteins. If the protein is, for example, present in urine, the binding of the antibody to it could be used to bring about a colour change.

10 How could monoclonal antibodies be used as a pregnancy test? **Hint:** during pregnancy specific proteins are found in the urine.

11 Cancer cells are often impossible to detect by X-ray. How could monoclonal antibodies help X-rays to track down a cancerous growth? **Hint:** metal atoms can be detected by X-rays.

Answers

1

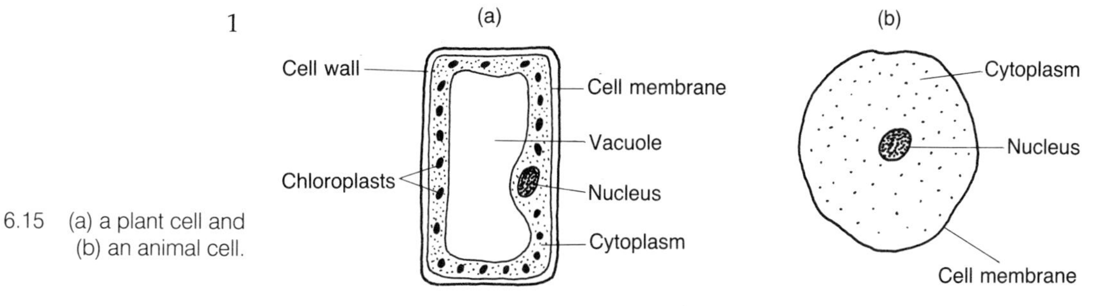

6.15 (a) a plant cell and (b) an animal cell.

2 Find an agent that would bring about the destruction of the cell wall/membrane. Bleach works in this way.

3 When storing and preserving, make sure that the spores are unable to germinate, for example by freezing. When the food is defrosted it should be eaten immediately so as not to allow the number of bacteria to rise. Cooking may not destroy the spores.

4 Bacteria that can cause food spoilage. These are the same bacteria that recycle our nutrients. They are saprophytes and feed by secreting enzymes onto the surface of the food. The enzymes then digest the food, liquefying it in the process, so that the bacteria can absorb the nutrients. This is why the texture of food alters when it has 'gone off'. Another example is bacteria that cause disease – pathogens.

5 The skin is an impermeable barrier unless it is cut. When we breathe in, dust and microbes are trapped by mucus and swept back to the mouth by tiny hairs called cilia. The digestive system destroys bacteria with the stomach acid or the digestive enzymes.

6 AIDS victims are unable to replace white blood cells. Every time they get an infection, the white blood cells that die in the destruction of the bacteria are not replaced. When the white blood cell count becomes dangerously low, the patient is defenceless and even a common cold can be a killer.

7 They must not be broken down by our digestive enzymes. This would render them useless.

8 a Nitrogen, an element essential to all animals and plants, is made available to them because of the work of bacteria in the soil. Bacteria help to break down proteins from dead animals and plants into ammonia, which is then turned into nitrates by the nitrifying bacteria in the soil. Plants take up the nitrates through their roots and make protein. This plant protein becomes a source of protein for animals.

b Some bacteria recycle nutrients by means of decay. For example, carbon dioxide from dead animals and plants is released into the atmosphere by saprophytes and fungi.

9 Citric acid and acetic acid (vinegar) are made through microbial action. Bread making has used yeast for centuries. The yeast ferments sugar in the dough and, in the process, produces carbon dioxide. This gas causes the bread to rise. Many types of bacteria and moulds convert milk to cheese. Microorganisms allowed to grow on cheese as moulds give it a distinct flavour and texture as in, for example, Stilton cheese. Lactic acid bacteria turn milk into yoghurt.

10 Certain proteins are only present in the urine during pregnancy. A monoclonal antibody that is specific for these proteins would bind to them in the urine. The antibody–protein complex could bring about a colour change, giving a positive result if the urine changed colour.

11 A monoclonal antibody could be developed that is specific for proteins on the surface of cancer cells. A metal could then be attached to the antibodies, which would show up on an X-ray. The antibodies and their attached metals would accumulate wherever cancer cells are present.

Glossary

acetylcholine: A chemical that transfers nerve messages across a synapse.

acquired immunity: The immunity that we build up from birth as a result of encountering disease-causing organisms.

aerobic respiration: The release of energy from glucose, by combination with oxygen.

alleles: Alternative forms of a gene that are found at the same location on the chromosomes of a homologous pair. They are responsible for the same characteristic.

anaerobic respiration: The release of energy from glucose, without oxygen.

antibodies: Chemicals that are produced by special white blood cells (leucocytes) in response to antigens. They help to destroy invading bacteria.

antigen: The protein that is found on the surface of a bacterium. Different bacteria possess different antigens.

asexual reproduction: Reproduction without sex. It involves only one individual – no gametes or sex cells are involved and the offspring are genetically identical to the parent.

ATP: Adenosine triphosphate. A high-energy compound in which the energy released from glucose in respiration is stored. It is found in all living cells.

bacteria: Single-celled microorganisms that possess a cell wall but no nuclear membrane.

binary fission: The way in which bacteria continually reproduce by division.

biotechnology: The use of living organisms or biological processes for the manufacturing or service industries.

blood: Fluid found in vertebrates that transports nutrients, oxygen and waste products around the body. In humans it contains 45% red cells and 55% plasma.

blue-green algae (Cyanobacteria): Organisms that are very similar to bacteria, but are able to make their own food by photosynthesis.

breathing: A forced ventilation of the lungs to allow the gas exchange required for respiration.

cell division: Where a cell reproduces or makes a copy of itself.

cell wall: The structure which surrounds and gives shape to the cells of plants and bacteria.

chlorophyll: A green pigment found in plants which absorbs energy from sunlight to be used in photosynthesis.

chloroplast: Structure found in many plant cells which contains chlorophyll and where photosynthesis takes place.

clones: Genetically identical organisms formed by the asexual reproduction of one individual.

compensation point: The light intensity at which photosynthesis and respiration occur at the same rate in a plant.

consumers: Organisms that consume other organisms for food.

continuous variation: The gradual transition between two extremes in a population, for example from very small to very tall.

cytoplasm: A jelly-like material surrounding the nucleus of a cell.

decomposers: Organisms (usually soil bacteria and fungi) that cause the decay of dead organisms and release mineral nutrients into the soil.

diffusion: The random movement of molecules, atoms and ions from a region of high concentration to a region of lower concentration.

dihybrid cross: The production of offspring from two individuals that differ in two ways.

diploid: Describes a cell or organism with a full set of chromosomes.

discontinuous variation: Type of variation where a character has two or more distinct forms with no 'in-betweens'.

DNA: Deoxyribonucleic acid. The material of inheritance – the genetic material of a cell.

dominant gene: The gene whose characteristic will be inherited by the individual in the presence of its allele.

ecosystem: The living organisms and their environment in a certain area.

effector: An organ or cell that carries out an action in response to a stimulus.

endocrine system: A system of glands in an animal that produces chemicals (hormones) which are secreted into the bloodstream to control bodily functions.

eukaryotes: Organisms whose cells possess true nuclei.

exponential growth: A form of population growth in which the population doubles over a fixed time period.

F_1 generation: The first generation from a particular cross.

F_2 generation: The second generation from a particular cross – the offspring of the F_1 generation.

fermentation: The conversion of sugar into alcohol and carbon dioxide, often by yeast, by means of anaerobic respiration.

flaccid: The state of a plant cell that has begun to plasmolyse and, because of losing water, becomes less firm.

food chain: A 'chain' that connects animals with their food and with the animals that eat them.

full plasmolysis: When a plant cell loses so much water by osmosis that the plasma membrane pulls away from the cell wall and the contents shrivel.

gametes: Special types of cells that fuse during fertilisation. They contain half the number of chromosomes found in the other cells of the organism.

gametogenesis: Cell division that results in the production of haploid cells or gametes (meiosis).

gametophyte: The haploid stage during the life cycle of a plant. Its job is to produce gametes.

gene: A unit of heredity. A segment of DNA on a chromosome which controls the development of a particular characteristic.

genetic engineering: The insertion of a sequence of DNA that codes for the production of a particular protein into the DNA of a microorganism.

genotype: The genes of an individual.

gland: An organ that produces a specific hormone.

haploid: Describes a cell or organism with half the full number of chromosomes.

heterozygous: Describes an organism with different alleles of a particular gene, for example a person might have one allele that codes for blue eyes and one that codes for brown eyes.

homeostasis: The processes within the

body that maintain a constant internal environment.

homozygous: Describes an organism with identical alleles of a particular gene, for example a person might have two alleles that code for blue eyes.

hormones: Chemical messengers that travel around the body in the bloodstream. They are secreted from glands and affect specific 'target' organs or sites.

hydrostatic pressure: The pressure blood develops when entering a capillary. It is higher at the arterial end than at the venous end.

incipient plasmolysis: When a plant cell loses sufficient water to cause the plasma membrane to just pull away from the cell wall.

isotonic: Describes solutions that have the same osmotic potential because they contain the same salts dissolved to the same concentrations.

locus: The position of a gene on a chromosome.

meiosis: The type of cell division that gives rise to gametes or sex cells, which have half the full number of chromosomes. Sometimes called reduction division.

metabolic rate: The speed at which the chemical reactions of metabolism occur in an organism.

metabolism: The chemical processes taking place in a living organism.

mitochondria: Structures within cells that are the site of aerobic respiration.

mitosis: The type of cell division that produces an identical copy of a cell.

monohybrid cross: The production of offspring from two individuals that differ in only one characteristic.

mutation: A change in a gene or a chromosome that arises spontaneously.

natural immunity: The defence systems we possess to prevent bacteria getting into the body.

nervous system: A network of cells that detect, and coordinate responses to, changes in the internal and external environments of an organism.

neurone: A nerve cell.

nucleus: The part of the cell, enclosed in a membrane, that contains the genetic material or DNA.

organ system: A group of organs that work together to perform a specific task, for example the lungs, kidneys, liver and skin make up the excretory system.

osmoregulation: Control of water content and salt concentration in the bodies of animals.

osmosis: The overall movement of molecules through a semi-permeable membrane from a region of low concentration of a solute to a region of higher concentration of the solute.

partial pressure: The pressure that a particular gas in a mixture contributes to the total pressure of the mixture. It depends on the percentage of that gas in the mixture.

pathogen: A bacterium that causes disease.

phagocyte: A cell that is capable of engulfing particles from its surroundings in order to destroy them.

phenotype: The physical appearance or characteristics of an organism.

photosynthesis: The process by which green plants make carbohydrates from carbon dioxide and water using energy from sunlight.

plasma: The fluid component of blood containing mostly water, dissolved solutes and clotting protein.

plasmid: A tiny circle of DNA found in the cytoplasm of certain bacteria.

plasmolysis: Loss of water from a plant cell by osmosis.

pressure potential: The tendency for water to be pushed out of a cell.

producers: Organisms which produce food, i.e. green plants. They are the first organisms in a food chain.

prokaryotes: Primitive organisms whose cells do not have true nuclei.

protoplast: The contents of a plant cell between the plasma membrane and the sap vacuole (including the cytoplasm, nucleus and small vacuoles).

receptor: A structure in an organism that detects a stimulus.

recessive gene: The gene whose characteristic can be masked or hidden by the presence of a dominant allele.

reflex: A fast, involuntary reaction to a stimulus involving at most two or three neurones.

respiration: The release of energy from carbohydrates which happens in every living cell.

response: A change or action that is brought about by a stimulus.

ribosomes: Tiny particles of RNA that are found in the cytoplasm of cells. Their job is to manufacture proteins for the cell.

RNA: A long-chain molecule very similar to DNA which carries 'messages' from the DNA to the ribosomes.

semi-permeable membrane: A barrier which is porous, so that molecules which are small enough can pass through. Larger ones pass through slowly or not at all. Sometimes called a plasma membrane.

sexual reproduction: Reproduction involving sex – the production of sex cells, or gametes, followed by fertilisation, giving rise to a completely unique individual.

solute potential: The ability of a solution to lose water by osmosis.

somatic cells: All the cells in an organism that have a full set of chromosomes.

spore: A small cell that can grow into a new organism.

sporophyte: The diploid stage during the life cycle of a plant. Its cells undergo meiosis to produce cells that grow into a haploid structure or gametophyte.

stimulus: Any change in the internal or external environment of an organism that is large enough to be detected by a receptor.

stomata: Openings in the surface of a leaf that allow gas exchange to take place.

tissue fluid: Plasma minus the proteins and the cellular components of blood.

toxin: A poisonous substance produced by disease-causing bacteria.

turgid: The state of a plant cell that has taken in water by osmosis so that the cytoplasm has swollen and pushes firmly against the cell wall.

ultrafiltration: The process by which small molecules and ions are filtered out from larger molecules and cells under pressure.

variation: The combination of new characteristics in an organism.

water potential: The ability of a cell to lose water by osmosis.

zygote: The cell produced immediatly after fertilisation. When two gametes, for example a sperm and an egg, unite, a zygote is the diploid cell that results.